PAPA MARRIED A MORMON

PAPA MARRIED
A MORMON

JOHN D. FITZGERALD

PRENTICE-HALL, INC.

ENGLEWOOD CLIFFS

for Mamma and Papa

FOREWORD

"John D.," Mamma said to me when I showed her a copy of the magazine containing my first published short story, "promise me that some day you will write a story about the little people who built the West—the people like Papa, Uncle Will, Uncle Mark, Aunt Cathie, Bishop Aden, Hal Gentry, Grandpa and Grandma Neilsen. Write a true story about the Mormons as Papa knew them, as I know them, as you know them."

The promise was forgotten until after her death. Mamma was a souvenir collector. We found several trunks in our attic filled with diaries, letters, newspaper clippings, prize ribbons won at fairs, school report cards, programs of the operas Mamma saw in Denver on her honeymoon, our baby clothes and other mementoes of some particular event in Mamma's or Papa's life that held a sentimental value.

I remembered my promise as I relived Papa's and Mamma's lives when I read the diaries, the love letters, the old newspaper clippings. I was swept into the past as I fondled these by-gone treasures and looked at the photographs and tin-types in the family album. I made a story outline and compiled hundreds of notes about "the little people who built the West." However, our entry into World War II brought an abrupt end to the work. The house was sold. The family scattered. The promise was again forgotten.

Fourteen years later when preparing to move to another city, my sister found the story outline and notes in an old trunk. She sent them to me. The ghosts of the past paraded by me, reminding me of my promise. The story of the miners and the Mormons as Papa, Mamma and I knew them, still had to be told, and could be told only by some use of poetic license so that the story would be of the people who made Utah history and not history *per se.*

Now, there are left only the tombstones, man's briefest biographies.

Now, there are left only the diaries, the turning of each musty page like the opening of a door into a long vacant room.

Now, there are left only the newspapers, jaundiced and brittle with age.

Now, there are left only the love letters, faded and so crisp they crumble even at a loving touch.

Now, there are left only the failing memories of the very aged.

Now, there are left only the skeletons rattling in the family closet.

But, now the promise is fulfilled.

John D. Fitzgerald

Contents

[ix]

PAPA MARRIED A MORMON

PROLOGUE

Mᴇxɪᴄᴏ became a Spanish possession two hundred years
before there was a United States of America. In the spirit
of the times, the Catholic priests carrying the Cross and the
Spanish soldiers carrying swords began the conversion of the
natives to Catholicism. A string of missions was built northward along the Pacific Coast for a distance of five hundred
miles and northwest as far as Santa Fe, New Mexico.

To consolidate this huge empire the two terminals had
to be joined. The Escalante Domingues Expedition failed;
but a later expedition established what became known as the
Old Spanish Trail. This ran from Santa Fe through the
southeastern corner of what is now Colorado, across what is
now Utah and Nevada, on westward to San Bernardino, California, and from there to the Pueblo of Los Angeles.

Spanish traders traveled this trail for half a century without building a single settlement along the way. The major
business of these traders when traveling westward was buying and stealing male Indian children and adults. On arriving
at the Pueblo of Los Angeles, they sold these helpless Indians
into slavery to work on Spanish ranchos or to be sent to
Mexico to work in the mines. The trip eastward differed

only in the sex of the Indians. Female children and adults were bought or stolen to be sold as slaves upon arrival in Santa Fe. These female Indians were sent to Mexico to work as domestics or in the fields.

The War of 1845 between Mexico and the United States reduced this empire by one half. Two years later Brigham Young led the Mormons into the Great Basin, later known as Utah Territory. The Latter-Day Saints took the bleak, barren land that nobody wanted and wrested from it food, shelter and clothing. They planted trees, built homes and, with irrigation, pushed back the desert along the Old Spanish Trail.

The Latter-Day Saint religion teaches that the American Indians are Lamanites, descendants of a long lost tribe of Israel. The Saints were the first white men who did not covet the land, the treasure or the person of the Indians. They called the Lamanites "brother," and sought them out only to convert them to Mormonism and attempt to civilize them.

Dixie, to the Mormons, is that portion of Southern Utah Territory colonized by them. In the year 1854, Brigham Young addressed a group of volunteers for an Indian Mission to Dixie. The purpose of the Mission was to build a settlement at the mouth of Red Rock Canyon and do missionary work among the Paiute Indians.

"Learn their language," Brigham Young exhorted the members of the Mission, "and this you do more effectively by living among them as well as by writing out a list of words. Go with them where they go. Live with them, feed them, clothe them and teach them in their own language. They are our brethren, we must seek after them, commit their language, get their understanding."

Those were days when boys became men in their teens.

Ephraim Aden, a big-boned, tall, gaunt-faced youth of twenty was chosen Captain of the Mission. His lean, homely appearance was accentuated by what remained of his right ear. All of the ear but the lobe had been torn off by a bullet in a hunting accident. He had formed a habit of reaching for his ear and, finding it gone, gently pulling on the remaining lobe.

The Mission consisted of twelve wagons, thirty horses and mules, six cattle, eight cows, twenty-six men. They traveled southward along the Old Spanish Trail to Cedar City. From Cedar City they struck out over ground that had never known the touch of a wagon wheel. They had traveled only a few miles when a band of Indians mounted on small ponies surrounded the wagon train. The Indians spread a blanket in front of the lead wagon. The Chief of the tribe pointed at the blanket and began shouting in a guttural voice.

Captain Aden, realizing that the Indians were demanding tribute before they would permit the wagon train to proceed, ordered bread, bacon, flour and tobacco placed on the blanket. The Indians picked up the tribute and rode away.

Their first contact with the Paiutes impressed the members of the Mission with the big job that lay ahead of them. The Indians were filthy dirty. The odor emanating from their bodies was nauseating. This feeling was mitigated by the knowledge that the "Diggers," as they were called on the other side of the mountain range, were much more unkempt and uncivilized than the Paiutes they'd just met.

Three days' journey brought the Mission to the mouth of a canyon they named Cottonwood. Here a camp was made while a dugway was built up the canyon to the top of the plateau. Upon completion of the dugway the camp was moved to the top of the plateau. The construction of a dugway down Red Rock Canyon on the other side of the bench was begun.

From the rim of the eastern side of the plateau the view was uninterrupted for as far as the eye could see. Here the Wasatch promontories ended abruptly. The desert below was strewn for miles with grotesque rock formations, left from volcanic upheavals, which reached up from the sands like the gnarled hands of the damned. The rain and wind had carved fantastic shapes out of the red sandstone, and these added to the bleakness and unearthliness of the scene.

Winfred Judd, Recorder of the Mission, after viewing this foreboding sight made this entry in his journal: "I find it hard to believe that man, beast or plant could survive in such a God-forsaken place."

The judgment of the scouts who had chosen the location for the colony was vindicated when the dugway down Red Rock Canyon was completed. The land at the mouth of the canyon was virgin and fertile. A creek fed by many springs wound its way down the canyon. It became a mere trickle by the time it reached the bottom, but a dam could be built with flumes to carry the water over the sandstone formations.

There was some concern about the wind, which at times blew so hard that it hurled sand against the faces of the members of the Mission until they were flecked with blood. When this concern was voiced to Captain Aden, he replied: "Brothers, I say this to you, that on this site chosen by the scouts and approved by President Young, we shall build a colony if we have to plant a seed at a time and stand upon it until it takes root."

A survey was made of the new townsite with lots laid off and plotted. The numbers of the lots were placed on slips of paper and put into a hat. Each member of the Mission drew a slip of paper entitling him to a lot six by twelve rods within the townsite. Later each member drew slips from a hat which entitled him to one acre of ground outside the townsite for farming, and four acres of desert land which could be converted to pasture land by irrigation. The town was named Adenville in honor of the Captain.

Their first shelters were dugouts. A hole six feet deep and twelve feet square was dug in the ground. It was covered with a roof made from cottonwood poles slanted at a twenty-two degree angle, with bundles of rushes placed between the poles and held in place by willows. A foot of dirt was shoveled on top to keep out the rain, snow and cold. The dugouts had no windows. A door was fashioned from a piece of canvas stretched on poles and hung with hinges made from the bark of willows. Beds were constructed by driving four corner posts into the dirt floor. Black willow poles were split in two to serve as bed slats. These were covered with pine branches providing a mattress. Pillows were made from the flugg of cattails which grew along the creek bank. A plank placed across the posts at the foot of the bed was used as a table. A piece of rag tied to a button in a shallow dish of grease provided light. There was an abundance of greasewood, sagebrush, rabbit brush and mesquite for fuel. These dugouts were the first homes of almost all pioneer Mormon colonists.

A log meeting-house chinked with mud was erected and dedicated after all the dugouts were completed. During the first church services held in the meeting-house, Captain Aden gave thanks that only two men had been lost since the Mission had left Salt Lake City. One member had been killed during the construction of the dugway up Cottonwood Canyon; the other had died of pneumonia.

The names of the remaining members were placed on slips of paper in a hat. They drew lots to see which six members would leave immediately to begin the missionary work among the Indians and which eighteen would remain to build the canal and the dam. There were no exceptions in these drawings. Captain Aden and Winfred Judd were two of the six names drawn.

The Missionaries left the following day. They traveled northward on horseback along the foot of the plateau for three days before arriving at a temporarily deserted Indian village. Judd made the following entry in his journal concerning this first Indian village: "We shall have no trouble locating the Paiute villages. The stench of one can be smelled for a mile or more."

Fires were still smoldering in the village and several dogs were running around. The Missionaries spread a blanket before the Chief's wikiup which was covered with tule rushes, placed leaven bread, dried fruits, beads and tobacco on it, and sat down to wait.

Two hours passed before a young Paiute of about twenty years came down from the hills. He stopped within hailing distance and called to the Missionaries in Spanish, asking who they were. Judd, who spoke Spanish, called back that they were Latter-Day Saints come to seek their brothers, the Lamanites. The youth disappeared and returned shortly with his father, who was Chief of the tribe, and several old men who were members of the council.

Captain Aden presented the Chief and his son with gifts, while the members of the council squatted around the blanket and began cramming the food into their mouths. The Chief's son's meager knowledge of Spanish was a fortunate happenstance, although the story he told of how he had acquired it was almost unbelievable—he claimed he'd been stolen by a more powerful tribe and sold to the Spanish traders when fourteen. At the Pueblo of Los Angeles he had

been sold as a peon to work on a rancho. After four years
of slavery, he'd escaped and all by himself made his way
across the desert back to his tribe.

The Chief invited Judd and Captain Aden into his wikiup.
Judd speaking in Spanish, with the Chief's son translating
into the Uto-Aztecan language of the Paiutes, told the Chief
the history of the Lamanites. He showed the Chief the pages
in the Book of Mormon wherein the history of the Lamanites
was recorded from plates of gold.

The Chief snatched the Book of Mormon from Judd, strode
from his wikiup and called the tribe before him. He held
aloft the book and proudly told the tribe that their history
was written in it. He said the Missionaries were sent by the
great Indian God Shenowab to help them because they were
brothers. He ordered the squaws to prepare a meal and
invited the Missionaries to eat with him and his council.

Captain Aden watched the squaws bring water from a
stream in willow baskets lined with pine gum. The water
was poured into clay dishes, and hot rocks were dropped in
to make it boil. They cooked a food that was dark grayish
in color and looked as if it had chunks of bacon in it. The
odor, even from a distance, was repugnant.

The Missionaries sat in a circle in the Chief's wikiup with
members of the council. A wicker basket containing the
grayish colored food was passed from hand to hand with
each diner taking a fistful. With stoic calm the Missionaries
ate the food, not discovering until later that what they
thought was bacon was in reality bunches of matted ants.
This was the forerunner of many meals for which the Missionaries needed strong stomachs. They found, for instance,
that the only parts of small animals like rabbits which
weren't eaten by the Paiutes were the fur and the bones.
Head, entrails and all were cooked by the Indians and de-

voured with relish. Grasshoppers were roasted, or after being driven into a pit and dried, ground into a meal from which a sort of biscuit was made. The Missionaries stuffed themselves with berries, acorns, sunflower seeds, cactus fruit, parched corn, squash, yam and sego lily roots so they might eat as little meat as possible.

One week after their arrival they received permission from the Chief to baptize and confirm the entire tribe. They knew it would be difficult because the Paiutes had an aversion for water. When the Missionaries washed or bathed in the creek, the whole tribe would line the banks and laugh at them. None of the tribe had taken a bath since they were born. It took a great deal of coaxing to get the Paiutes to consent to immersion in the creek water.

Soon after, a member of the council became ill. Captain Aden discovered that the Paiutes immediately seemed to understand the "laying on of the hands," to heal the sick. This confirmed his belief that the Lamanites were descendants of the long lost tribe of Israel and that the ritual had been either handed down to them from generation to generation, or had come to them by instinct because it was a part of their past.

The first time the Missionaries sang a hymn all the Indians including the Chief fled to the hills. It wasn't until this happened that the Missionaries learned that the Paiutes didn't know how to hum or sing. After overcoming their fear, the Indians made nuisances of themselves every time the Missionaries sang a hymn by insisting on looking into the Missionaries' mouths and poking their dirty fingers inside to find the thing that made the music.

Captain Aden and his followers remained in the camp for three months during which time they learned enough of the Uto-Aztecan spoken language and sign language to spread the

word of the Gospel of the Prophet Joseph Smith, the founder
of Mormonism, among the Lamanites. It wasn't until they
were ready to leave that they discovered the Paiutes didn't
know the meaning of a handshake. The Indians insisted on
placing their wrists in the Missionaries' hands.

A seven-day journey northward brought the Missionaries
to a much larger village, where they arrived at a most in-
opportune time. The tribe's Chief, Sanchem, was dying. The
medicine man and the council of the tribe refused the Missionaries' request to administer medicine or even "lay on
the hands."

Captain Aden and his followers were forced to sit idly by
and witness a carnage of savage orgies attendant on the
Chief's illness and death. The first day the Missionaries were
in camp two Indian boys, a squaw and seven horses stolen
from another tribe were killed as a sacrifice to make the
Chief well, and there followed six bloody days of pagan
sacrifices of human beings and animals before the Chief died.

With helpless horror the Missionaries watched the Chief's
five squaws beaten to death by other squaws. They were
appalled when eight young boys, thirty horses, and two
young Indian maidens were slaughtered as a sacrifice. The
nightmare was climaxed when a twelve-year-old Indian boy
was buried alive with the dead Chief after being told he was
to watch over him.

The Missionaries spent three months in the village before
returning to Adenville. They all felt discouraged. Judd gave
voice to this when he wrote in his Journal:

The Paiutes on this side of the mountain range have been
preyed upon by stronger tribes. Their terrible fear of Spanish
slave traders has driven them into desolate regions where they
have taken up life as animals and not as human beings. They
are amongst the most degraded peoples in the world. They

know not the meaning of pity or love. They are congenital
thieves and it is as impossible to teach them stealing is a sin
as it would be to tell the sparrow he must not snatch the worm
away from the robin. They are lazy and indolent. They are
barbaric but lacking in the courageousness of the Sioux or
Apaches. The conversion and civilizing of the Paiutes will take
many, many years. I agree with Captain Aden that we must
give most of our attention to the young.

Twenty years later Judd noted in his Journal:

Our success in converting and civilizing the older Paiutes has
succeeded only to the point where we have made them discon-
tinue their barbaric practices of human sacrifice. Sometimes I
think the only reason the older members of the tribes offer
themselves up for rebaptism each year is to obtain a clean shirt.
The older members have been Christianized only to the extent
that they come knocking on our doors at Christmas time carrying sacks and crying: "Creesmas geeft." The smaller and weaker
tribes which have moved closer to Adenville for protection present a problem. The only thing they won't steal is a cow. For
some strange reason they consider a cow unclean and will not
drink milk or eat butter. Dear Lord, never has a cow been so
maligned. We have succeeded in teaching them cleanliness to
a certain extent.

Our biggest success has been with the children and younger
Paiutes. We have taken the children into our own homes and
raised them with our own children. We have established a Mission School and were surprised at the aptitude for learning some
of the children displayed.

We have placed Missionaries with all the tribes on a rotating
basis. They are charged with the health and well-being of the
tribe as well as their spiritual welfare. They have taught the
tribes farming, irrigation and agriculture. It is still necessary
for us to furnish each tribe with a considerable amount of produce from our storehouse to insure them an adequate diet.

Although our progress has been slow, we feel that we have
accomplished a great deal. We have proven to the Paiutes that

we are their friends and brothers. We have driven away the terrible fear they had in them of the white man and Spanish slave traders. There remain many years of work to be done with the Lamanites.

The colonization of Adenville flourished. In the year 1877, as our story opens, the population was over one thousand. There were log cabins or adobe houses for every family. A grist mill, a woolen factory, a tannery and a soap factory were all producing for export to Salt Lake City and other communities. Eighty acres of cotton, forty acres of corn, ten acres of vineyards and sixty acres of wheat were under cultivation. The dam which used to "go out like the wash," every Monday was rebuilt and was strong enough to resist any flash flood. The canal, which had given so much trouble owing to gopher holes, was now reinforced with willow growths along its banks, and permanent wooden flumes had been built over all sandstone formations.

Upon completion of the beautiful Tabernacle made from red rocks quarried in the canyon, Adenville was made a Ward with Ephraim Aden as Bishop, fourteen high priests, eight seventies, forty elders, six priests, seven teachers and twenty deacons.

Two great calamities befell the community in 1877. Its residents were still in a state of shock and grief over the death of their beloved President, Brigham Young, when a prospector accidentally stuck his pick into a sandstone formation in Red Rock Canyon just two miles above Adenville and discovered horn silver where silver had previously not been known to exist. The hell-roaring mining camp of Silverlode was born.

1

UNCLE WILL'S ARRIVAL
IN SILVERLODE

M̲y̲ ᴜɴᴄʟᴇ, Will D. Fitzgerald, despised the weak. He believed that if there had been only the strong in this world, life would have been a better contest. This trait in his character manifested itself during his boyhood when he would fight only bigger and older boys.

A grown man crying over the death of a child was to Uncle Will a weak man unable to face reality. A man who killed another man when he knew he could beat him on the draw, was to Uncle Will a weak man, because there was no danger to himself. He sought excitement and adventure with the same intensity of purpose that most men seek economic security. He had many friends, although he never fully gave his hand in friendship to any man, because of his mental reservations about the weakness he saw in all men.

His agnosticism began in the Confessional when he was ten years of age. He was confessing his part in flooding a farmer's field so it would freeze over and enable him and his friends to skate upon it. The next day as they enjoyed their sport the farmer, a fat Dutchman, tried to chase them off his property. He was no match for the boys on skates and he kept falling on his portly backsides. At the memory

of this, Uncle Will burst out laughing. Father O'Leary
reached around the Confessional and boxed the boy's ears.
From that moment Uncle Will became a silent critic and
doubter of God and religion.

He was fifteen when he defied his father and refused to
attend church any more. Grandpa Timothy took his son into
the barn of their home for a whipping. This time, Grandpa
Timothy promised himself, he would make this son of his
cry. He removed the birch rod from its place on the wall and
motioned for his son to lie down over the whipping barrel.

Instead of obeying, his son said, "You've whipped me for
the last time, father."

Grandpa Timothy raised his arm only to find his wrist
grasped with fingers of steel. He exerted all his strength,
but slowly felt his wrist being twisted until the pain caused
him to drop the birch rod. So infuriated that he raised his
fist to strike his son, he found himself knocked to the ground
with a powerful blow to his solar plexus.

"I don't want to hurt you, Father," his son said slowly,
"but you've whipped me for the last time. There isn't a boy
or man in this town I can't lick."

Later Grandpa Timothy appealed to his eldest son, John,
for help in disciplining Will. He regretted this when he
watched the younger boy, fully a head shorter and twenty
pounds lighter, beat John in a fist fight in the barn.

Uncle Will did not wear his agnosticism as a policeman
wears a badge. He was an individualist, and he believed all
men are entitled to believe anything they wish. He never
ridiculed God or religion. This refusal of his openly to
mouth his agnosticism stemmed from the fact that he was
a gambler and considered it an "ace in the hole." Since he
never spoke out against God, if by chance there should be
a God, it would be in his favor on Judgment Day.

He was sixteen when he began his preparations for leaving the ancestral home in Boylestown, Pennsylvania, and going out West. He received a Sharps revolver, a holster and shells from a mail order house, and at the same time he began to frequent Murphy's Tavern and participate in the gambling games. The first time Will entered the tavern, Mr. Murphy, the proprietor, tried to put him out, only to receive a terrible shellacking.

Mr. Murphy appealed to Grandpa Timothy, who in turn sought the help of the town marshal. When the marshal ordered the boy to leave the tavern, Uncle Will rested his hand on the butt of the Sharps revolver and told the marshal he'd shoot if the law enforcement officer tried to put him out of the tavern. The marshal knew of the hours Uncle Will had spent practicing drawing the gun from its holster and shooting at targets. He reported to Grandpa Timothy that he would have to kill the boy or be killed.

Grandpa Timothy resigned himself to having his son spend all his time in the tavern or down by the river practicing with the gun.

On his seventeenth birthday Uncle Will announced that he was leaving for the West. Grandma Annie cried out in protest to her husband, "Please don't let him go, Timothy. He is just a child going out into that wicked and dangerous wilderness."

Grandpa Timothy was skeptical. "If you must feel sorry, Annie, feel sorry for the Wild West. It's the Fitzgerald curse. There is one born in every generation."

Life to Uncle Will was a gamble and the reason he became a gambler. He found it easy to win from other men because his face was never the mirror of his thoughts. For two years he worked in gambling establishments from St. Louis to California. When he considered himself proficient in his chosen profession he became a lone wolf. He killed his first man a few months later in Denver. A miner had accused him of cheating in a card game. Uncle Will looked across the table at the man. "You can apologize or go for your gun, stranger. It is immaterial to me." The miner died before getting his gun from its holster. That night Uncle Will left Denver for Utah Territory.

There was a pattern to his wanderings. He always turned up in mining camps right after a big strike had been made. He was in Frisco, Utah Territory, when he learned of the Silverlode strike. At that time he'd killed seven men, four of these in arguments over card games and three who were seeking a reputation as gun slingers.

His total possessions at the time consisted of his clothes, several thousand dollars he carried in a money belt, and the ornate jeweled holster that held his pearl-handled revolvers. Uncle Will, like the gamblers of today who generally have a big diamond ring they can pawn when luck goes against them, had the jeweled holster made by a Denver jeweler after he had won several thousand dollars in a poker game. The value of the precious stones in it was another "ace in the hole" of his.

During the first few months after the rich strike at Silverlode there was no law except that of the six-shooter. By the time the murders per day had reached an average of ten, the citizens called a mass meeting at the camp ground. Hal Gentry, a former outlaw who had turned peace officer and had been marshal of mining camps in Utah and Colorado Territory, was verbally elected Marshal. Frank Baker, an attorney, was elected City Judge. The absence of a court-house and a jail did not halt justice. Suspects were tried on the spot or in one of the saloons. The sentence was either hanging—from a rafter in Tanner's Livery Stable—or being tarred and feathered and ridden out of town on a rail.

Marshal Gentry was a big man who wore his two hundred pounds of flesh well. He carried a chamois and could usually be found using it to polish one of his Peace Maker Colt revolvers. He had a habit of interrupting the polishing to use the barrel of the gun to scratch his ear or nose. He believed himself to be the fastest man on the draw in Utah Territory, but he realized that it was more than a one-man job to keep the peace in Silverlode. Therefore, he swore in several local citizens as deputies without badges. The demise of many a gun slinger was due to this system of deputies. Marshal Gentry met every stage and made the rounds of all saloons and gambling halls daily. When he spotted any gun-man he knew or any man who boasted of his prowess with a six-shooter, Gentry would give the man until sundown to leave town.

Blackie Lanell was one of the many victims of the Marshal's system of deputies. He rode into Silverlode one day and after several drinks in the 66 Saloon began to brag of the many men he'd killed. When ordered by Marshal Gentry to be out of town by sundown, Lanell just laughed and said as how he guessed he'd stick around. Blackie happened to be one man who was as fast on the draw as he claimed to be. But he made the mistake of deciding he needed a shave and haircut.

Gabby Harnett, the barber, was a banty-sized deputy who loved to talk. His barber shop was stocked with every preparation for growing hair on the market, and Gabby was his own best customer. He spent hours in front of the mirror rubbing hair tonic on his bald pate.

He put a towel around Blackie Lanell's neck and proceeded to give the gunman a haircut. The work was considerably slowed down by Gabby's loquacity. Gabby had finished shaving one side of Blackie's face just as the sun sank below the mountain range. Gabby laid down his razor, removed a Smith & Wesson revolver from a drawer, placed the end of the barrel in the gunman's ear, and pulled the trigger as he said: "I kill you in the name of the law."

The Mormons living in Adenville had refused to trade with the citizens of Silverlode until the mine superintendents arranged a meeting with Bishop Aden. The Bishop wrote a report to the church hierarchy in Salt Lake City of the fantastic prices that could be obtained for meat and produce. He was granted permission to trade with the Gentiles. Bishop Aden laid down certain conditions. The Aden Irrigation Ditch which ran from one side of the valley to the other was to be the dividing line between the two towns. He would send two men daily into Silverlode to canvass the various places of business and take orders; the food and goods ordered would be delivered the following day and be paid for in cash. The entire trade agreement would be rescinded if any Gentile crossed the irrigation ditch into Adenville without first receiving permission from the Mormons. As a result of this agreement, Adenville enjoyed a prosperity unequalled by any other Mormon community.

The man who boarded the stagecoach out of Salt Lake City for Silverlode had a hundred and eighty pounds of sinewy muscle well distributed over his six-foot frame. His hands were long with tapering fingers. His wide-spaced brown eyes set above high cheek bones were expressionless, whether he laughed or frowned. His mouth was a trifle large with white even teeth. He wore a tailor-made serge suit, and a checkered brocade vest with a heavy gold watch chain dangling from it. His black hat, pushed back on his head, revealed black curly hair. His mustache was evenly waxed. A very narrow black necktie tied in a bow knot hung down over his shirt front. Around his waist he wore a hand-tooled leather holster and belt studded with precious gems. The legs of his trousers were tucked neatly into highly polished black boots.

When the stagecoach was ready to begin the ascent up Cottonwood Canyon, he approached the driver and asked if he might ride with him, because the ladies in the stagecoach objected to his smoking.

Lem Owen rolled a wad of tobacco to the side of his jaw. "Sure thing, stranger," he said revealing brown stained teeth beneath a gray mustache that dripped with tobacco juice. "We got to wait for a spell. Ain't but four places to pass on this dugway. Sam, that's my guard, rides ahead. We wait for him to give us the high-sign. See that bend up there. That's Sam now waving the white flag. Means he'll hold any wagons coming down till we get there." He clacked his tongue and started the four-horse team up the grade.

The passenger offered the driver a cigar which was refused, then lit one for himself. "Name's Fitzgerald. Will Fitzgerald."

Lem Owen grunted. "Reckon you're one of the gamblin' fellows."

"Anything against gambling, old timer?" Uncle Will asked.

"Nope," Owen shrugged. "Last gambling fellow rode with

me was dead before sunup next day. Silverlode's one of the toughest camps in the Territory. If you ain't good at gambling without cheating, and if you can't back your play with a fast draw, maybe Silverlode ain't the town for you."

"Don't worry about me, old timer." Uncle Will laughed.

Owen gave his full attention to the horses until they reached the top of the plateau. When Uncle Will remarked that the top of the plateau was good grazing country for sheep and cattle, the driver shrugged. "You'll never see sheep or cattle till the mines peter out."

During the descent down Red Rock Canyon, Owen became more communicative. "See that dam the other side of the canyon? Before Silverlode, the Mormons had a dam on this side. After Silverlode the water got so polluted by the time it reached Adenville it wasn't fit for man nor beast. The Mormons built a new dam and a canal down the other side of the canyon. Some said it couldn't be done. But they did it. Wait'll we round this point. There, look at that flume carrying that water over that ravine. Stands all of ninety feet high. Highest in the Territory. Them Mormons can make water run up hill. Plumb crazy about water and trees. There's a saying in the Territory that when two Gentiles meet they have a drink; but when two Mormons meet, they plant a tree, build a dam and a canal. Damnedest tree planters since Johnny Appleseed."

Uncle Will wet his mustache with his tongue. "An unusual breed of men, all right. I often wondered why they didn't develop the mines. It was Abe Lincoln, I believe, who once said, 'Utah will yet become the treasure house of the nation.'"

Lem Owen shook his head. "Brigham Young forbid them to mine except for what they needed themselves. Strange about a lot of things. Don't drink nor smoke. Don't even drink coffee. They make a wine called Dixie wine which they sell, but they never drink it. Stranger, you ain't been honestly drunk till you get drunk on Dixie wine." He nodded his head forward. "When we round that bend, you can see Silverlode."

Uncle Will, like most men, looked upon a strange city through eyes that affected his own personal future. He saw the hundreds of tents in Tent City as the stagecoach crossed the planked bridge over Indian Creek. To him, they meant hundreds of miners with money and the big tents meant saloons and gambling halls. As the stagecoach wound its way down the main street of Whiskey Row, which reeled and twisted through the town like a drunken miner, Uncle Will saw only the Fairplay Saloon, the 66 Saloon and the Silver Dollar Saloon. He paid no attention to the Silverlode Bank, the Post Office, Wells Fargo Office, or Tanner's Livery Stable, which was on the corner of Whiskey Row and Corry Street. Alighting from the stagecoach and claiming his luggage, he walked across Whiskey Row to the Emporium, and strode along the wooden sidewalk until he arrived at the Miner's Hotel, which the driver had recommended to him.

After washing up and changing shirts, he ate in the Miner's Cafe. As he left the restaurant, he lit a cigar and walked toward Corry Street. He saw only the Canton Cafe and the homes of the mine superintendents on Corry as it stretched northward. He crossed Whiskey Row and walked south on Corry Street, passed the blacksmith shop, and continued to the camp ground. Retracing his steps, he again stood at the intersection of Whiskey Row and Corry Street. Looking eastward, he saw the Silverlode Mining and Development Company's building on the right corner. Beyond it was the small building of *The Silverlode Advocate,* a shoe repair and harness shop combined, and Ma Burke's Boarding

House. On the left side was the Whitehorse Saloon, which stood on the corner of Whiskey Row and Corry Street. Gabby Harnett's Barber Shop and Bathhouse was between the saloon and the Silverlode Hotel and Restaurant.

It was just after twilight and he could see the lights of the Mormon town of Adenville on the other side of Aden Ditch. He recalled Lem Owen's advice as he crossed Corry Street toward the Whitehorse Saloon: "If you're looking for small stake games, try the gambling halls and saloons in Tent City. If you're looking for medium-like stake games, try the Fairplay or 66 Saloon. And if you're looking for the really big stake games, ain't no place but the Whitehorse. Nat Breen, the owner himself, takes a hand in the big stake games. A fellow can win or lose thousands. One more word of advice, stranger, Nat Breen killed two men on account of those big stake games."

Uncle Will pushed open the swinging doors and entered the Whitehorse Saloon. The first thing that caught his eye was a giant hunchback with a bullet-shaped head covered with thick, black, matted hair. The misshapen creature had a watery, vulgar mouth, and hairy hands; and his small gimlet eyes were glued to the back of a man at the bar.

The object of the hunchback's attention was a small statured man with a clean-shaven aristocratic face, the thin nose of which always seemed drawn up disdainfully. Doc Tethers had eyes that were watery blue, with a sullen and defiant look in them. His silvery gray hair was curled tight against his well-barbered head. He carried several large linen handkerchiefs in his pocket which he used when he got one of his coughing spells. They were flecked with blood each evening. He was spending this night, as he had spent every night since his arrival in Silverlode, with the hunchback he called Peter, standing at the Whitehorse bar. He shunned all company and drank until he fell in a stupor on the floor. Then the hunchback would pick him up in his hairy arms and carry him home.

Uncle Will walked across the sawdust covered floor to the long mahogany bar, with brass rail and spittoon in front of it, and ordered a drink of straight bourbon whiskey.

The bartender, a man called Horseshoe Jim, had a diamond horseshoe tie pin on his shirt-front. He wore a toupee, and when perspiring or excited would push it to the back of his head. Between his teeth he carried an unlit pipe. His placid face never changed expression. He was a teetotaler and never drank anything stronger than an occasional glass of cider from the barrel on the end of the bar.

The mahogany back bar had thick round end pillars and heavily scrolled designed cutwork across the top, from which hung a sword in a sheath. The marble top was covered with tiers of sparkling glasses, and whiskey and liquor bottles.

Uncle Will turned around, resting one heel of his boot on the brass rail and hooking his left thumb in the belt of his jeweled holster. A stairway ran upstairs to a balcony which completely encircled the saloon, providing private dining booths. The space on the second floor over the storerooms was utilized as rooms for the dance hall girls, and a suite of rooms for the proprietor.

A man in a derby hat and smoking a cigar was playing a piano. It was too early for the entertainment; but the kerosene lamps with tinned reflectors were lit on the small stage. Four huge glass chandeliers with kerosene lamps hung from the beams in the ceiling. The wall of the other side of the saloon was adorned with the mounted heads of Rocky Mountain sheep, mountain lions, deer, elk and two big grizzly bears.

Uncle Will was impressed. It was the most plush saloon

and gambling hall he'd ever seen in a mining camp. Leaving the bar, he spent an hour watching the various gambling games in progress. He bought chips and began playing roulette, but he kept his eye on the big stake poker game until he saw real money being bet.

From the July 1 edition of The Silverlode Advocate, *a weekly newspaper published every Friday in Silverlode, Utah Territory. Dave Powell, editor and publisher.*

THE PASSING AWAY OF NAT BREEN

Death, as it must come to most men who accuse other men of cheating in a card game, came to Nat Breen, late proprietor of the Whitehorse Saloon, at eleven-fifteen A.M. last Wednesday morning. Breen's premature demise was due to a stranger who was not only a better poker player but also faster on the draw.

The shooting was the culmination of a fifteen hour poker game. The stranger who arrived Tuesday afternoon on the stagecoach entered the Whitehorse Saloon about six P.M. At eight P.M. he took a hand in the big stake poker game. By midnight, he had won over five thousand dollars, and at this point Nat Breen took a hand in the game. One by one the other players dropped out of the game. The two men played all through the night and into the morning. At approximately eleven A.M. Wednesday morning the stranger had broken the saloon bank, having won more than twenty thousand dollars.

Nat Breen challenged the stranger to one hand of showdown poker with the stakes the stranger's winnings against the Whitehorse Saloon. The stranger accepted the challenge with the same cynical smile that had never left his face since the game began.

A new deck of cards was called for. Both players shuffled the deck and then cut high card for deal. The stranger won. He dealt the cards one by one face up. As the last card fell, the stranger became the owner of the Whitehorse Saloon by virtue of three jacks against Nat Breen's pair of kings.

Nat Breen was so indelicate as to suggest that the stranger's good fortune had not been attributable to luck or skill. He was foolish enough to back up this accusation by going for his gun. The stranger continued to smile. His hands never left the top of the table until Nat Breen touched leather. Then, with a lightning-like draw unparalleled in these parts, the stranger drew. Nat Breen was dead before he got his gun out of its holster.

All witnesses agree the stranger shot in self-defense and there was no evidence of cheating. *The Advocate,* in the interest of impartial reporting, reminds its readers that on two previous occasions Nat Breen lost the Whitehorse Saloon in poker games, only to retrieve same by accusing his opponent of cheating and then beating him to the draw.

The new owner of the Whitehorse Saloon has informed *The Advocate* he will remain in Silverlode. We can therefore stop calling him stranger and welcome to our midst Will Fitzgerald, new proprietor of the Whitehorse Saloon, lock, stock and barrel.

2

UNCLE WILL AT THE BATTLE
OF SILVERLODE

THE ACQUISITION of the Whitehorse Saloon put an end to Uncle Will's wanderlust. He took an auburn-haired dance hall girl called Queenie for his mistress, and they lived in a suite of rooms on the second floor of the saloon.

The Battle of Silverlode would never have taken place if Dave Powell hadn't thought Uncle Will was bluffing in a poker game. Powell, the editor and publisher of *The Silverlode Advocate,* had been a tramp printer until he received a legacy from an aunt. Casualties of newspapers in the Territory were exceeded only by the homicide rate, but this didn't deter Powell from buying a defunct newspaper press and type in Alta and moving it all to Silverlode.

He was a very fat man whose small ankles and feet were never meant to carry such weight. He could walk only a short distance and then had to sit down to rest his ankles and feet. His face was moon-shaped; he had a triple chin; and his drab brown hair was fast receding on his head. Usually he wore a black alpaca coat with wide arm bands on the sleeves.

He was a very heavy drinker, but a man who drank without seeking argument; he had the true journalist's gift of looking upon all persons and things objectively. His was one of the few newspapers in the Territory that was neither pro- nor con-Mormon. This impartiality enabled him to obtain subscriptions, advertising and printing from the Latter-Day Saints in addition to the Gentile business. The circulation of *The Advocate* at the time Uncle Will won it was 1,142 paid subscriptions at five dollars per year.

The usual crowd was in the Whitehorse Saloon that eve- ning: Horseshoe Jim with his diamond stick pin gleaming and his toupee pushed to the back of his head; Doc Tethers getting drunk at the bar with the hunchback watching him; Judge Baker with his shoulder-length white hair cascading from beneath his hat, and his porous cherry nose; Windy Davis with his small eyes on the lookout for a winner from whom he might cadge a chip for a drink. Windy never worked. He slept in the manger in Tanner's Livery Stable, and was a sort of town crier. When a fight, a shooting, or something of interest happened, he would run from saloon to saloon to broadcast the news and collect a drink at each.

Seated at the big stake poker game were Marshal Hal Gentry, polishing one of his guns with a chamois; Dandy Allen, the gambler, with his amethyst cuff links glittering under the overhead kerosene lamp; Uncle Will, with Queenie standing behind him; and Dave Powell.

The game went on, with other players taking a hand and then dropping out. At four o'clock in the morning, Allen, Powell and Uncle Will were the only players left. Powell was winning what to him was considerable money—almost one thousand dollars. Dandy Allen was dealing as he smoked a small Cuban cigar. He was a handsome man with a black hairline mustache, and dark hair that glistened from the pomade upon it. He threw his own hand in, saying, "I think you are all bluffing, Will, but I pass."

Dave Powell studied his hand and then slowly pushed his entire stack of chips into the center of the table. "I also believe you are bluffing, Will, but I will back up my belief with money."

Uncle Will felt the hand of Queenie on his shoulder. He smiled up at her. She was beautiful with her reddish eyebrows arched over brown eyes and her copper-colored hair fastened with a jeweled comb. Her green silk gown moulded itself around high breasts, a slim waist, and hips that stoked the flames of desire in men when she walked.

Uncle Will looked across the table at Powell. "I'll just call you, Dave, and raise you right back."

Powell smiled, his triple chin flopping as he did. "My only regret is that I haven't any more money."

Uncle Will ran a finger across his mustache. "I admire a man with the courage of his convictions, Dave. How much do you figure that newspaper of yours is worth?"

Powell shook his big head. "My intuition that you are bluffing is not strong enough to risk losing my livelihood."

Uncle Will had a way of gently jeering at people. "I'm either bluffing or I'm not. You are already in the pot for a thousand. I'm calling your raise and raising you back. Two thousand against *The Advocate*."

Powell took a handkerchief and wiped his brow. "I've studied you, Will, and the last time I saw you rub your finger across your mustache like that, you were really bluffing. I have no alternative but to call you."

Uncle Will laid down a diamond flush against Powell's three aces and became the owner of *The Silverlode Advocate*.

Dandy Allen removed the small Cuban cigar from his mouth. "You going to coddle those Mormons the way Dave has done, Will?"

The remark seemed to be the signal for miners, pros
pectors, dance hall girls, trappers and all the flotsam and
jetsam of a mining camp, to crowd around the table and
give Uncle Will advice.

A tall, raw-boned freighter held up his hand for attention.
"I heerd tell they brung in four wagon-load of wimmen last
week. Feller I knowed got a look at 'em. All young 'uns."

A grizzled miner spoke up. "T'ain't fair. Thar ain't nigh
nuff women to go 'round, and danged if some of them Mormons ain't got eight or ten wives."

For an hour Uncle Will listened to complaints about the
Mormons. Finally he held up his hand. "All right. Queenie,
get me pen, ink and paper. I'll write an editorial for *The
Advocate* expressing the opinions of all those present."

The following afternoon in the office of *The Advocate*,
Dave Powell tried to talk Uncle Will out of publishing the
editorial. "I admit that polygamy is wrong, but history has
proven that the more you persecute a religion, the stronger
it becomes. A religious belief isn't something you can change
overnight, like a political belief. I'm not defending the Mormons, Will, but if you leave them alone, they'll leave you
alone and give you their business."

Uncle Will got up from a chair and hooked his left thumb
in the belt of his jeweled holster. "Frankly, Dave, I don't
give a damn if every Mormon has twenty wives. My only
interest is in making money at the Whitehorse. My customers happen to be individually and collectively against
the Mormons. If printing this editorial will make my customers happy, there is nothing more to say."

"But," Dave Powell protested as he waddled his huge body
behind Uncle Will toward the door, "if you lose the Mormon subscriptions, advertising and printing business, *The
Advocate* will go broke."

"Don't worry about that, Dave," Uncle Will said over his shoulder. "I'll put you on a salary and use money from the Whitehorse to keep the paper going. This might be interesting. At least it will stir up a little excitement."

From the editorial page of the June 6, 1882 edition of The Silverlode Advocate. *Dave Powell, editor. Will D. Fitzgerald, publisher.*

VIOLATION OF AMERICAN WOMANHOOD

The anti-polygamy bill passed by the Congress of the United States in June of 1862, and the Edmunds Anti-Polygamy Bill passed in March of this year, apparently mean nothing to the Mormons. They are still preying on innocent women and girls, coercing and duping them into becoming polygamists' wives. The laws of the Government of the United States apply to all citizens regardless of religion. We demand that the Federal government enforce these laws, not by merely making an occasional arrest; but by having the Army, if necessary, make a simultaneous arrest of all polygamists.

We demand a halt to the use of a religious tenet to sell into legalized prostitution American womanhood. We demand an end to this Mormon practice of breeding bastards. We demand imprisonment of every Mormon polygamist and the freeing of their so-called wives from bondage.

Editorially yours,
Will D. Fitzgerald

The repercussions that followed the publication of the editorial were immediate. Latter-Day Saints and Jack Mormons cancelled their subscriptions and sent their printing to Salt Lake City. The Gentiles of Silverlode showed their appreciation by filling the Whitehorse Saloon to capacity. The compliments Uncle Will received from the Gentiles, and the increase in business at the Whitehorse, so pleased him that he wrote a fresh blast against the Mormons in each succeeding issue of *The Advocate*. He achieved what was really a free press. *The Advocate* was distributed free to anyone who would enter the Whitehorse Saloon and take a copy from the bar. Advertisements were printed free, and the only thing that had to be paid for was printing matter.

In October of 1882, Bishop Ephraim Aden held a secret meeting with the church hierarchy in the Adenville Tabernacle. He was a big man, well over six feet tall. His clean-shaven face revealed features that were plain and homely, but his bluish gray eyes seemed to compel attention when he looked at you. His hands were so large that his wives had to knit mittens for him. Sometimes he wore Indian moccasins because he couldn't buy shoes large enough for his feet. He had a habit of pulling at the lobe of his left ear—all that remained of it, that is, after it was hit by a bullet during his youth. His hair was prematurely gray, but there was the spring of youth in his step despite his forty-eight years.

"Brothers," he said, laying down a copy of *The Silverlode Advocate* on the long table, "we must put a stop to the atrocious lies this man Will Fitzgerald is printing about us Latter-Day Saints. He is accepting as facts every Gentile untruth that has ever been said about our religion. He is inflaming the Gentile and heathen population of Silverlode to the point where mass hysteria might take place and a mob of drunken miners descend upon us. He is attracting undue Federal intervention. We have boycotted his newspaper to no avail, because he uses some of the profits from his den of iniquity to subsidize it. The only way we can kill this serpent, Brothers, is to cut off its head. I have a plan."

The plan began taking shape just two weeks before general elections were held throughout the Territory. Prior to this time, the only elections ever held in Silverlode consisted of a town meeting at the camp ground. Some saloon keeper would nominate Hal Gentry for Marshal and Frank Baker for City Judge, someone in the crowd would second the motion, and both were elected by a voice vote.

Handbills were distributed by the Saints two weeks before election, proclaiming that the People's Party were entering a complete slate of candidates for county offices. This news drew considerable derision from the Gentiles, who outnumbered the Mormons two to one.

Uncle Will entered into the spirit of things, and printed handbills with a slate of candidates for the Liberal Party. With the exception of Hal Gentry for Sheriff and Frank Baker as District Judge, the list of candidates was meant to ridicule the People's Party. Windy Davis was candidate for county treasurer; other candidates were just as unsuited for their positions. Uncle Will had Dave Powell write humorous articles in *The Advocate* about how unfit for public office these candidates were. The whole election was being treated as a joke by the Gentiles; but they hadn't reckoned with Bishop Aden.

The battle of handbills continued right up to the eve of election day. The People's Party declared in one handbill that, if elected, they would stop all gambling in the county. Uncle Will countered with a handbill promising that if the Liberal Party were elected, they would ban the making of Dixie wine in the county. The Mormons issued another handbill stating that, if elected, they would ban all dance hall girls in the county. Uncle Will issued a handbill in rebuttal asserting that if the Liberal Party were elected, they would pass an ordinance forcing all Mormon females to wear chastity belts, with the single key for each belt to be held by the Sheriff and to be presented to a Mormon male only if he could produce a marriage license and take the Expurgatory Oath each time he asked for the key.

A tent was erected near Aden Ditch to serve as a polling booth. Both parties appointed ballot-box watchers. Election day arrived and before it was over the Gentiles were no longer laughing. The People's Party had won the election by forty-two votes. Bishop Aden's plan had worked. He had brought Saints from nearby and distant settlements under the cover of darkness and hidden them out in Mormon homes and on Mormon farms. On election day they all trooped to the polls and voted for the People's Party.

The newly elected Mormon Sheriff was a tall, thin, loose-jointed man named Hank Jeffers. Upon a direct appeal by Bishop Aden to Brigham Young he had been sent to Adenville when Silverlode was born. He had been a guard, a soldier in the Mormon Battalion, and a scout. During the first year in Adenville, when there hadn't been any law in Silverlode, Jeffers had killed eight gunmen who had invaded Adenville looking for trouble. He was a man without fear, and he proved it the day after he was sworn in as Sheriff.

He entered Silverlode alone carrying some handbills under his arm, and posted them on hitching posts, buildings and trees to inform the citizens of Silverlode that in keeping with their election promise all gambling was forbidden in the town effective at eight o'clock the next morning.

The next day Jeffers came to Silverlode wearing his guns. His first stop was the Whitehorse Saloon, where he arrested Uncle Will and took his prisoner back to court in Adenville, where Judge Potter fined Uncle Will two hundred dollars. During the day Jeffers arrested all the other saloon and gambling hall proprietors. They also were fined two hundred dollars. The Mormon Sheriff had trouble in only one spot, a small gambling place in Tent City, whose owner, a man called Snake Wilson, refused to be arrested and dared Jeffers to go for his gun. The Mormon Sheriff killed Wilson.

The following day Sheriff Jeffers again arrested all the saloon and gambling hall proprietors. This time they were fined four hundred dollars each and told the fines would be doubled the next time.

Uncle Will called a meeting of the mine superintendents and saloon keepers. The meeting took place around the big stake poker table in the Whitehorse Saloon. Some of the principals were seated at the table, others standing.

Uncle Will leaned back in his chair and hooked his thumbs in his jeweled holster. "You all know why you are here," he said. "Tomorrow Judge Potter will fine us eight hundred dollars. This is an old Mormon trick that has been used in other places in the Territory. They just keep doubling the fines until they put you out of business."

Lee Mulrein, proprietor of the Fairplay Saloon, pointed his cigar at Will. "Why don't you take them up on their proposition and close down that newspaper of yours? You ain't making any money out of *The Advocate* anyway."

Uncle Will seemed surprised as he saw the other saloon keepers nod their heads in agreement. "Just a minute, Lee. I don't know what proposition you are talking about."

Mulrein scratched his ear. "Then you are the only one

who don't. Jeffers told all of us that the arrests would stop as soon as publication of *The Advocate* stopped."

Uncle Will studied their faces as his lips drew back tight. "I'm damned if I'll do it. I'm damned if I'll kowtow to these Mormons. You leave me no alternative. I'm sending word to Jeffers that if he steps foot over Aden Ditch Bridge tomorrow morning, I'll meet him in the middle of Whiskey Row. And he'd better come shooting."

Dale Ferrin, Superintendent of the Silverlode Mine, hastily blew a cloud of cigar smoke from his mouth. He was a fastidious dresser, aping in fashion the eastern capitalists he served. He wore spats and carried a gold-headed cane. "We cannot countenance murder, gentlemen," he said as he dabbed a handkerchief to his brow.

Uncle Will exploded. "Don't be a damn fool, Ferrin. How long do you think you could keep miners, muckers and freighters in Silverlode without gambling, drinking and dance hall girls?"

Judge Baker rubbed a bony finger up and down the side of his porous red nose. "The demise you contemplate for Sheriff Jeffers would bring instant repercussions, Will. Jeffers is a duly elected officer of the law. If you kill him the Mormons could appeal for martial law and get it. Under martial law the saloons would be closed and the Mormons would achieve the same end result."

Ferrin leaned forward. "You are versed in the legal profession, Judge. We know the Mormons stole the election. Isn't there some way of petitioning for a new election?"

Judge Baker nodded. "There is a way out of our present dilemma. We can get up a petition for a recall and force a new election by demanding that all Mormons voting must take the Expurgatory Oath to qualify."

Uncle Will shrugged. "That would take time. We've got

to stop these arrests and fines at once. There must be a quicker way. It's unconstitutional."

"Exactly," Judge Baker said. "In the event we can prevent Jeffers from making any arrests under the pretense we are defending our constitutional rights, the federal courts in Salt Lake City will provide us with legal sanction. I suggest that Bishop Aden be advised that we shall defend our constitutional right to the pursuit of happiness—with bullets, if necessary—until a new election is held."

Editorial from the first Extra ever published by The Silverlode Advocate:

MORMONS DEFY THE CONSTITUTION OF THE UNITED STATES

The Constitution of the United States guarantees all citizens the right to life, liberty and the pursuit of happiness. The recent arrests and fines imposed upon the saloon keepers of Silverlode indicate that the Mormon Sheriff Hank Jeffers and the Mormon Judge Potter either haven't read this noble document, or consider the Latter-Day Saints to be immune from federal laws.

We declare all candidates elected by the People's Party in the recent election to be holding office illegally. We demand a recall and a new election subject to the laws of the United States. We demand that every Mormon who votes must take the Expurgatory Oath before the vote is counted as being valid. How many Mormons who voted in the recent election can or will take the following oath:

"And I do furthermore solemnly swear that I am not a bigamist nor a polygamist; that I am not a violator of the laws of the United States prohibiting polygamy; that I do not live or cohabit with more than one woman in marriage relation, nor

does any relation exist between me and any other woman which has been entered into or continued in violation of the said laws of the United States, prohibiting polygamy or bigamy."

This oath alone would have disenfranchised ninety percent of the Mormon votes cast in the last election. We therefore refuse to recognize Jeffers and Potter as duly authorized law enforcement officers.

The pursuit of happiness can entail many things, such as the right to engage in a friendly poker game. Jeffers and Potter have conspired to circumvent this right by arresting the saloon keepers of Silverlode and doubling their fines for each arrest, until it becomes unprofitable to operate gambling games. We shall defend this constitutional right to the death. I call upon the citizens of Silverlode to rally around the flag at the Whitehorse Saloon no later than eight o'clock tomorrow morning. No mines will work. Come wearing your guns and prepared to fight unto the death defending the glorious Constitution of the United States.

Editorially yours,
Will D. Fitzgerald

The extra was distributed gratis to every tent, shack, and place of business in Silverlode. By midnight the Whitehorse Saloon and all others along Whiskey Row were jammed. Old uniforms were dug out of trunks, the enmities of the Civil War forgotten as the Blue and the Gray stood at bars with their arms around each other. Chinese coolies who had helped build the railroad from California to Ogden came armed with knives. Irish immigrants who had helped build the railroad from the East to Ogden came armed with pick handles. Mexicans armed with stilettos mingled in the crowd.

Uncle Will assumed command of this motley army. He dispatched armed guards to patrol all roads leading into

Adenville to prevent infiltration by the enemy, and sent saboteurs to cut the telegraph line to Salt Lake City. Then he had Frank Baker draft a declaration of war against the Latter-Day Saints, warning them that if the ban on gambling were not lifted by noon of the following day, a state of war would exist between Silverlode and Adenville.

There were no fights or killings that night. The call to a common cause seemed to have united the citizens. It snowed lightly during the night, and the snow turned into a drenching rain with the morning.

Uncle Will had remained up all night waiting for word from the enemy, which never came. One hour before the noon deadline, he ordered a barricade thrown across Whiskey Row from the Whitehorse Saloon to the Silverlode Mining and Development Company building. Shouting, inebriated miners gleefully carried kegs of beer and whiskey into the street to build the fortification. Gabby Harnett removed a flag from the wall of his barber shop and placed it upright in the bunghole of a whiskey keg right in the center of the barricade. The piano from the Whitehorse was pushed to the wooden sidewalk.

When the men manning the fortification complained about the chilling rain, Uncle Will went from whiskey keg to whiskey keg, knocking out the plugs and inserting spigots. This produced more volunteers for front line duty than the barricade could accommodate.

Barnaby Smith pushed his derby hat to the rear of his head and began playing the nearest thing to a martial air he knew. Windy Davis, drunker than he'd ever been in his life, appropriated the sword and sheath from the rear bar of the Whitehorse Saloon, strapped it around his waist and swaggered onto the wooden sidewalk.

It was a magnificent spectacle. The wet flag making a

feeble attempt to stir in the light breeze. The drunken miners raising their voices in defiance as they sang "Glory,
Glory, Hallelujah," making up their own words if they
didn't know them. Windy Davis was deeply moved. He
unsheathed the sword, waved it gallantly and shouted:
"Don't shoot till you see the whites o' their eyes, boys." And
with that battle cry, he fell off the wooden sidewalk flat on
his face in the mud, where he lay until the battle was over.

Uncle Will was seated at the big stake poker table with
Hal Gentry, Dandy Allen, Frank Baker and Doc Tethers,
who had risen to this glorious occasion by remaining sober.
Peter the hunchback stood behind Doc's chair. It was five
minutes before the noon deadline when Butch Mears, driver
for a freighting company, pushed open the swinging doors
and shouted: "Here they come, carryin' a white flag. Damn
'em double, the white-livered cowards, and me spoiling for
a fight."

Uncle Will chose Hal Gentry and Frank Baker as his aides.
Climbing over the barricade, they walked down the ankle-
deep mud of Whiskey Row to meet the Mormons.

Bishop Aden, towering above them all, waited with Hank
Jeffers and Judge Potter until the Gentiles were facing him.
"We Saints are men of peace, not violence," he said as the
rain dripped from his black hat. "We received your declaration of war and submit to your surrender terms. The order
prohibiting gambling in the county is hereby rescinded."

Uncle Will knew when to press his luck. "That isn't
enough, Bishop. We've a petition signed by three thousand
citizens demanding a recall and a new election to be held
under the laws of the Territory of the United States Government. If Jeffers and Potter don't resign as of now, and
appoint Hal Gentry and Frank Baker in their stead pend-
ing a fair and square election, I'm leading an army of more

than a thousand men—armed to the teeth and spoiling for a fight—against Adenville."

Bishop Aden with visions of drunken armed miners running amok in Adenville did not hesitate. "We accept your surrender terms. However, might I suggest a counter proposal? You are not interested in extending the authority of Marshal Gentry or Judge Baker beyond the confines of the city limits of Silverlode, are you?"

Uncle Will shrugged. "We don't give a continental damn who runs things outside Silverlode."

"Then, we can make a just peace." Bishop Aden proved to be no slouch either when it came to pressing his luck. "Permit the elected county officials to remain in office and we give our word that we will not interfere by law or personally in the civic affairs of Silverlode."

Uncle Will looked at Frank Baker. "What do you think?"

Judge Baker pulled at his cherry red nose for a moment. "The special dispensation giving Silverlode exclusive jurisdiction over its own law enforcement would probably be for the best interest of all concerned. I haven't the least desire to begin arbitrating the water rights and other legal squabbles of Mormons in the county. And I feel assured that Hal here doesn't want to spend his time looking under beds for polygamists. The only additional condition I would make is that trade be resumed between the two towns on the same basis as it has been in the past."

Bishop Aden pulled on the lobe of his ear as he nodded his head. "We agree to those conditions. Our mission is ended amicably. Good day, gentlemen."

It was just as well the Mormons refused to fight. When Uncle Will climbed over the barricade to announce the complete surrender of the enemy, less than a hundred of the brave defenders of the Constitution were sober enough to cheer him and follow him into the saloon to celebrate the victory.

That was how my Uncle Will fought and won the Battle of Silverlode. You won't find an account of it in any history book, which seems unfair to my uncle. After all, he was defending the Constitution of the United States.

3

THE MIGRATION TO AMERICA

GIVEN ENOUGH GROG or provocation, any Irishman can look you in the eye and trace his ancestry straight back to the kings of Ireland. If told often enough, the lie is gradually accepted by the tellers as the truth. This is probably what happened to my family. My great-great-grandfather evidently had to top a claim by some other Irishman and claim our family were direct descendants of Maurice, a knight who came with Strongbow to Ireland at the request of Dermot MacMorrough to help him regain his Kingship of Leinster in 1169 A.D.

Maurice's descendants spread over the four provinces of Ireland, and at one time more than fifty lords and barons owed them fealty. The Geraldines, as they were later known, although of mixed Norman and Welsh origin, became more Irish than the Irish themselves, and fought the English down through generation after generation. My great-great-grandfather claimed that Lord Edward Fitzgerald, who was arrested by the English and died of his wounds in prison in 1598, was an ancestor of ours. My great-great-grandfather used the family crest on his stationery with the motto, "Crum Aboo," a war cry meaning onward to victory.

Thomas Fitzgerald, the infant heir from whom the Earls of Desmond were descended, would have perished in his cradle in a fire, had not a pet monkey broken his chain and saved the child's life. Later, Thomas added the monkey to the family coat of arms.

My own research has failed to prove the family claim to such noble ancestry, though I did trace them back several generations in an attempt to verify the family curse. That the Fitzgeralds fought the English generation after generation there was no doubt. An ancestor named Dennis Fitzgerald was captured by the English. He informed on six of his friends to save his own life. The six men were caught in an ambush by the English and killed. Dennis was found murdered a few days after his release by the English. Legend has it that the fathers of the six betrayed men called upon Dennis' father, James Fitzgerald. They pronounced a curse on the family that one male in each generation for six generations would die violently or in disgrace without benefit of confession and the last rites as an expiation for Dennis' cowardice.

James Fitzgerald loathed the English so much that he was twice as bitter about his son's cowardice as the bereaved fathers of the men his son had betrayed. He decreed that all his male descendants for all time to come would bear the middle name of Dennis to keep the disgrace and shame of the cowardice of one Fitzgerald alive in the family forever.

The curse prevailed in the next generation when the son of Dennis' brother ran away to sea and was later hanged as a pirate. In the following generation a son was arrested for smuggling and killed in an attempted escape. The curse continued into the next generation when a son fell off his horse while drunk with grog, and broke his neck.

My great-great-grandfather had two sons, Thomas Dennis and Charles Dennis. Thomas Dennis was the "lost one" of that generation. He did nothing but drink and play with any maid who had the right sort of a gleam in her eye. The maid's station in life meant nothing to him. He was in a barn with the wife of a tenant farmer when the husband locked the doors and set the barn on fire.

Charles Dennis more than made up for his brother. He fought the English as only a Fitzgerald could fight them. He had a price on his head. My great-great-grandfather worried that the family strain would be wiped out if this son were lost, and so prevailed upon Charles Dennis to escape from Ireland and go to America to perpetuate the family.

Charles Dennis was smuggled aboard a ship that took him to Hamburg, Germany, where he boarded a boat for the United States. His destination had originally been Boston, where he had distant relatives, but his meeting on the boat with Karl Weigland and family changed that. He was only twenty-two years of age and very homesick. Karl Weigland, his wife and two daughters, Hilda and Gertrude, adopted him. During the voyage, he learned to love them and eagerly accepted their invitation to accompany them to Philadelphia. Pooling the money his father had given him with Karl Weigland's, they purchased several acres of land in the Lehigh Valley.

The combination of the German's sense of thrift and passion for hard work, with the imaginative daring of the Irish, made them prosperous. As their farm produced more and more wealth, they bought more land in the valley. They wrote to relatives and friends across the sea about the fertile land and the great opportunity America offered. German and Irish immigrants poured into the valley. In time a town grew up around a crossroad near a farm owned by John

Boyle, and the town became known first as Boyle Corners and later Boylestown.

John Boyle had one daughter and three sons. Charles Dennis married the daughter, Catherine. She gave birth to two sons, Sean Dennis and Timothy Dennis. A baby girl was lost during childbirth and Catherine could have no more children.

But the curse had followed the family to America. Sean Dennis was sent to Boston to be educated. Relatives wrote that he was not attending school and squandering his money in debauchery. Great-grandpa Charles Dennis shrugged off these letters with the expression that every young man is entitled to sow a few wild oats. He had forgotten about the curse until he received word that Sean Dennis had been killed in a drunken brawl.

Great-grandma Catherine never let either of her sons forget they were part Boyle. She instilled in them that they were descendants of poets, writers, notaries and men of letters. It was she who had insisted that Sean Dennis be educated in Boston because it was the home of culture. After Sean's death she concentrated all her attention on her younger son, Timothy Dennis.

They say that Great-grandpa Charles Dennis passed away from a broken heart—he did die prematurely at the age of forty-one. Great-grandma Catherine, determined that her son would carry on the Boyle tradition of being men of letters, sent Timothy Dennis to Boston. When he completed his education, he bought a printing press and hired a printer.

Grandpa Timothy Dennis Fitzgerald did not need his mother's coaxing to know that he did not want to be a farmer. He was overjoyed with the thought of becoming the editor and publisher of a newspaper. The fact that it wouldn't pay the printer's salary meant nothing. His mother had conditioned him into thinking of all art as being non-profitable, and as they were comparatively wealthy, he embraced the idea. It was many years before *The Boylestown Gazette* became a paying proposition.

Despite his income from real estate and other investments, Grandpa Timothy never considered himself a success until *The Boylestown Gazette* was making money, and it was not until then did he begin earnestly looking for a wife. A few months later he married Annie Lakey, daughter of the village apothecary, and member of a deeply religious family. Annie's two brothers became priests; she herself was convent raised. The only arguments Grandpa and Grandma had were over religion. Grandpa Timothy was a tolerant person viewing all religion objectively; Grandma Annie was perhaps bigoted in many respects.

They had five children: John Dennis, Will Dennis, Thomas Dennis, Josephine and Catherine. At an early age John, the eldest, signified his intention of becoming a priest. The second eldest, Will, was only eight years old when Grandpa sadly shook his head and said to his wife, "He is the Godless one, Annie. Thank God, it will be the last of the lost ones."

When Grandpa Timothy told her about the curse, she laughed. "He's just a boy, Timothy. He'll grow out of it."

"No, Annie," Grandpa Timothy said sadly, "he is the one, all right. No matter how hard I whip him, he never sheds a tear or even whimpers. I cannot make him obey me. I have never once heard him say that he loves you or me."

Tom, the third eldest son, was entirely different from his brother Will. He was obedient, always showing his love for his parents, and his attachment to his mother was very strong. When she'd admonish him to go out and play, he'd reply that he would rather just sit and look at her because she was so beautiful.

Otherwise his childhood was normal. He teased his sisters and fought with his brothers, especially Will. Though he didn't care much for fighting or wrestling, he trained industriously in the gymnasium his father had built for the boys in the barn, and applied himself to the art of self-defense as a protection. His brother Will was always fighting and licking some older boy, who in turn sought revenge on Tom, and so Tom knew he would never have any peace until he could best his older brother. He never did get proficient enough to outbox his brother Will, but he could often win from him in wrestling.

When he was sent to the Academy in Harrisburg his homesickness was mitigated by the knowledge that for a while he wouldn't have to fight all the boys his brother Will licked. He was a good pupil, and one of the most prized letters his father ever received came from Tom's English teacher, who wrote in part: "The boy has a way with words and should be encouraged along literary lines."

During the summer vacation after his brother Will had gone West, Tom was forced to fight almost every boy in town, for all the boys Will had licked demanded satisfaction. He took several beatings, and after such encounters his father would say: "Were you afraid, son?"

Tom would truthfully reply he hadn't been afraid. He knew the bloody nose or black eye would soon heal, and in the fullness of time all the boys in town would have had an opportunity to avenge themselves.

His father would pat his shoulder and say, "It isn't whether you win or lose that counts. The only thing that matters is whether you were afraid."

Tom's character was moulded by two extremes. From his

mother he learned compassion, only to hear his father say
that pity is wasted on some people. From his mother he
learned that charity is divine, only to hear his father say
that charity begins at home. From his mother he learned
that revenge belongs to God, only to hear his father declare
that if a man hits you, you should hit him back. From his
mother he learned religious intolerance, only to hear his
father say emphatically that intolerance is the handmaiden
of ignorance.

He was sixteen when scandal rocked the little town. A
girl named Doris Brown gave birth to an illegitimate child
and named the son of a very prominent Catholic family as
the father. Tom overheard his mother say to his father,
"What can you expect from a Methodist?"

"Now, Annie," his father had protested, "that isn't fair.
The girl might be a Methodist, but the boy she claims to
be the father of the child is a Catholic."

"Nonsense," she replied. "The girl is just saying that because the boy's people have money."

This religious intolerance of his mother confused Tom.
When his oldest brother John announced his intention of
becoming a priest, he asked him: "Are you doing it for
Mother, John?"

His brother shook his head. "No, Tom, I'm doing it because I've wanted to be a priest since I first served as altar
boy for Father O'Leary."

Tom shook his head. "You are older and must be a very
wise person to want to be a priest. There is something I
can't talk about even to Father O'Leary and it bothers me
a lot. It's Mamma. Did you ever notice that when anything
happens to anybody who isn't a Catholic, right away Mamma
says, 'What can you expect from a Lutheran,' or whatever
religion besides Catholicism the person belongs to? But when

anything bad happens to a Catholic, Mamma will find all sorts of excuses for him. Now, Papa is entirely different. Papa says that you can no more stop sin from cropping out in people of all religious beliefs than you can disease."

John smiled. "Mamma is just Mamma. She doesn't mean it the way it sounds. Who was the first to offer to adopt Doris Brown's baby and give it a home when her own parents were going to disown her? Who was it made Papa go down and get Stanley Carter out of jail on bail after he beat his wife? Mamma is just Mamma, and you can't change her."

"But it confuses me," Tom said earnestly. "I want to be a good Catholic, but I can't find it within my mind or heart to believe that anybody who isn't a Catholic is bad."

"If you did believe that, Tom, you would not be a good Catholic. I once felt about Mamma's intolerance as you do; only unlike you, I went to Father O'Leary about it. He gave me a single sentence that removed all confusion and doubt from my mind. Father O'Leary said, 'The Catholic Church is the Mother Church and all religions are windows in the Mother Church. And if you break one of these windows, you desecrate the Mother Church.'"

Tom patted his brother on the shoulder. "John," he said smiling, "you're wise enough to be a priest, all right."

Tom's career had been chosen for him by his father. From the time he'd had the privilege of helping his father at the newspaper, the boy had thought to himself that if he could only grow up to be a man like his father, his cup of life would be full.

He eagerly accepted his father's choice of a college after graduating from the Academy in Harrisburg. That fall he enrolled at Loyola College in Baltimore, where he learned more than the arts, sciences and history from his Jesuit teachers; he was taught tolerance, justice and the love of the brotherhood of man. Very studious, he was probably considered something of a prude by his fellow students, though he accepted their invitations to visit their homes on week ends and an occasional holiday. He met their sisters and being a handsome youth could have made several conquests, but there was an intangible barrier between him and all the girls he met. He could feel no emotion toward them except that of friendship. His classmates chided him for being a big brother to every girl.

As his character began to crystallize, he set up certain precepts by which he would live. His belief in Catholicism would not tolerate a single standard of morals. Many times when his father or brothers had gently admonished him because he wasn't going steady with a girl, his mother would come to his defense. "Do not let them disconcert you, son. For every man there is just the one right girl in this world. Some day you will meet her, and when you do, you will know instinctively that she is the one girl for you."

His attachment for his mother was so strong that this thought became a fixation with him. He believed that as surely as he breathed, he would one day meet the girl he would marry, and when he did, he would know it the moment he saw her. The continence he placed upon himself was predicated upon his belief that when he did fall in love, there would be no sordid episode in his past to defile that love.

From the time he was a boy, he had enjoyed reading and searching for knowledge. Having always felt that the written word was the most creative of the arts, he knew after his graduation from college the kind of a journalist he would be. He would speak out earnestly for the things in which he believed; but would also listen attentively to those who disagreed with him. He would judge men by the contribution they made to science, culture, social and economic progress, tolerance, patriotism, spiritual leadership and their regard for the well-being of their fellow-men. He would seek only the good in men; but denounce the evil in them whenever he found them evil.

His father obtained him a position as an apprentice on a Philadelphia newspaper, where he was tested by being forced to hunt for type lice, spend hours on the hell box, and work twelve to fourteen hours a day. After six months as a printer's devil, he was promoted to copy boy. One month before his year was up, he was permitted to accompany reporters on assignments.

He returned to Boylestown where his father let him do most of the leg work in gathering news and soliciting advertising. After one year of this, his father permitted him to write an editorial of his own choosing for *The Gazette*. It was a proud day for Tom. Choosing as his subject Capital Punishment, he denounced it as contrary to the will of God, and made a fervent plea for a convicted murderer awaiting execution in a Philadelphia jail. His father was shocked by the subject chosen for a small country weekly; but kept his word and printed it.

Tom had been working on *The Boylestown Gazette* for two years when the death of his mother changed his entire life. Grandma Annie lay on her premature deathbed with cancer draining her body of life. All that could be done had been done. There was nothing left but to pray and to wait. Many times while unconscious she cried out the name of her son Will. Just a few minutes before passing into a coma, from which she departed this world, she became suddenly conscious, and her mind very lucid.

She looked up from her pillow into the faces of her loved

ones. She smiled at her eldest son, John. It was good to have a priest in the family. She smiled at her two daughters who were fingering their rosaries while tears ran down their cheeks. Josephine was married to a good Catholic man, and pregnant. Catherine, the youngest, was a beautiful girl on the threshold of womanhood, a devout Catholic and would one day make some Catholic man a good wife. Grandma Annie looked at the foot of the bed into the haggard, drawn face of her husband. Never had a woman known such love, tenderness, kindness and devotion from a man. Her tired eyes sought the face of her son Tom. It was to him she wished to speak.

It was the lost one, the Godless one, the laughing one, who made her cry out against her approaching death. She knew she would have no rest unless someone she could trust was watching over her son Will. She could see him coming home with fish on a reel and offering himself up for a whipping because he'd played truant from school. She could see him with his clothes torn and his eyes blackened, but grinning because he'd won a fight against a bigger boy. She could hear him arguing with his father about religion and God. She remembered the many times his father had taken him to the barn for a whipping and how each time she'd prayed that the boy would cry. If only he would cry! She could see his empty place at the dinner table and know he was at Murphy's Tavern.

Prayer, faith in God, and belief in Catholicism would insulate and protect all her loved ones but the lost one. She beckoned her head toward Tom. He dropped to his knees and folded her pale hand between his own.

"My son," she said, "I want you to promise me something."

He kissed her hand. "Anything, Mamma. Anything."

She smiled weakly. "I want you to go out West and find

your brother. I want you to promise me you'll watch over him and take care of him."

"But Mamma—" he started to protest.

She shook her head slowly, "I know you all believe that Will is dead because he hasn't written in years. I would have felt it and known if he were dead. I have prayed to the good Saint Jude to watch over the lost one. Now I am dying, but I cannot die in peace unless I know you will find your brother and watch over him."

"I promise, Mamma. I promise."

"Thank you, my son," she said, and, smiling, fell into a coma from which she never regained consciousness.

4

PAPA GOES WEST

At the time of his mother's death, Tom was a young man with a high indented forehead etched with jet black curly hair which had a pronounced cowlick he was constantly pushing back. His mouth was large and generously furnished with big white even teeth. His aquamarine eyes, parted by a patrician nose, always seemed filled with an intense curiosity. His voice was oratorical, arresting and earnest, as if each word he uttered were the most important and sincere he'd ever spoken. He was a big man, weighing over two hundred pounds and standing six feet three inches tall.

The day after the funeral, the family gathered in the parlor of their home, a very empty home it seemed with Grandma Annie gone.

Grandpa Timothy leaned back in his rocking chair. "I'm sorry your mother extracted such a promise from you, Tom. I feel quite certain that when and if you do find your brother, it will be the last thing he will want."

Tom stood in the center of the room with his black curly hair just inches from the chandelier. He hooked his thumbs under the lapels of his coat and rocked on his heels as he spoke. "That I shall find Will, if he is alive, I haven't a single doubt, although it may take years. That I shall remain with him, whether he wishes me to do so or not, I haven't a doubt. I shall be my brother's keeper and fulfill the promise I made to Mother. I shall go out West and find my brother, and when I do, there I shall put down my roots. I would appreciate it very much, Father, if you would advance me a part of my inheritance for expenses. I also ask that you give me your consent and blessing."

Grandpa Timothy nodded. "You have both."

John put his arm around Tom's shoulders. "It is a big country, Tom. I may be able to help. I will write letters to all Catholic parishes and missions in the West. Keep in constant touch with me by post. I would suggest, as a starting place for your search, that place in Colorado Territory where Will wrote his last letter. Josie or Catherine can find the letter for you."

In his search for his brother Tom traveled from Colorado Territory to California and back. Nine months after leaving Boylestown he received a letter from his brother John advising him to go to Salt Lake City and contact Father Farley there.

Upon his arrival in Salt Lake City, Tom located the only Catholic parish there and was shown into the rectory by a housekeeper. After introductions were over, Father Farley opened a drawer in a desk and removed a newspaper, which he handed Tom. It had been printed on a Ramage hand press and consisted of two sheets 7½ by 10 inches.

Father Farley nodded toward the newspaper. "I recalled

a letter I received from your brother when a misguided parishioner brought me this. I say misguided, because he thought the information about the Latter-Day Saints could be used by our church. Needless to say, I severely reprimanded the man and gave him penance to do. If you will note, the masthead of the newspaper lists a Will D. Fitzgerald as publisher. The name of the newspaper is *The Silverlode Advocate*. Silverlode is a mining camp in the southern part of the Territory.

"Thank you, Father," Tom said. "I shall leave at once. I can't help having my personal doubts that this could be my brother, because he hated journalism. However, the middle initial in the name is very significant. I am very grateful, Father."

It was a cool spring day in March when the stagecoach braked to a screeching stop in Silverlode. A drummer and Tom Fitzgerald were the only passengers. The drummer claimed his valise and sample case from the top of the coach, and started walking across Whiskey Row toward the Miner's Hotel. He had reached the center of the street when his bowler hat went sailing from his head as the loud cracking sound of a whip was heard. The drummer picked up his hat and walked over to the front wheel of a freighter. He looked up at the driver of the eight-mule team.

"I'm sorry, Mister Mears," the drummer said tipping his hat, then proceeded on his way to the Miner's Hotel.

Tom watched this bit of by-play while he claimed his luggage. He followed the drummer toward the Miner's Hotel, conscious of his bow tie, long-tailed coat, tight-legged pants and the bowler hat on his own head. He, too, had reached the center of the street when his own hat went flying from his head as the sound of a cracking whip was again heard. As he retrieved his hat, his large mouth grew grim. He picked up his suitcases and walked over to the freighter.

The driver flexed his wrist and expertly knocked a horse-fly off the rump of one of the mules in the lead team with his bull whip. He was a heavy-set man, very broad across the shoulders and chest. He shoved a dusty sombrero to the back of his head and through his brown-stained teeth spat tobacco juice which splattered over Tom Fitzgerald's pearl-buttoned shoes.

"Name's Butch Mears," he said in a nasal voice, "you plumb forgot to tip your hat to me. Fust thing all Dudes learn when they get to Silverlode is to tip their hats to Butch Mears."

Tom placed his hands on top of the wagon wheel. "You handle that whip like an expert," he said smiling.

Mears swung the whip back and forth just inches from Tom's face. "Yep, best mule-skinner in the whole dern Territory."

Tom grabbed the whip, giving it a strong jerk. Mears caught by the leather throng around his wrist was tumbled into the street. Tom moved in fast, pouncing on Mears, removing his gun from its holster, throwing it under the freighter. He grabbed the driver's wrist and pulled the leather throng of the whip over it. Jumping away from Mears, he threw the whip under the freighter.

"Now, Mister Butch Mears," he said smiling, "if you can fight your way to your whip, I'll let you knock off my hat again."

Windy Davis, who was sitting on an upturned keg in front of the 66 Saloon, ran inside, shouting, "Fight! Fight!" He collected his drink and ran down Whiskey Row to the Whitehorse Saloon. After collecting his drink from Horseshoe Jim, he walked over to the big stake poker table, where Uncle Will, Hal Gentry, Frank Baker and Dandy Allen were seated. "Butch Mears is goin' to slaughter a Dude. Butch is liable to kill him."

Uncle Will motioned for Horseshoe Jim to give Windy another drink, then went into the street followed by the others. They arrived just as Butch and the Dude had finished stripping to the waist. Uncle Will pushed his way to Butch's side and asked what the fight was about.

"Just going to learn this damn Dude some manners, Will. Would'ya believe it, this Dude refuses to tip his hat to me. Now I claim that ain't no way for a Dude to go on living."

Uncle Will took a long look at the stranger. "He's a fair-sized man, Butch. Maybe you bit off more than you can chew."

"Hell's fire, Will, I eat Dudes like him for breakfast."

Dandy Allen, the gambler, edged his way up beside Uncle Will. "You wouldn't want to bet on it, would you, Will?"

Uncle Will shook his head. "Didn't say I'd back my opinion with money."

Dandy Allen held up his arms, his amethyst cuff links flashing in the sunlight. "Did you hear that, boys," he shouted at the rapidly gathering crowd. "First time I ever knew Will Fitzgerald to hedge a bet."

Uncle Will hooked his thumbs in the belt of his jeweled holster. "Since you force me, Dandy, I've got a thousand dollars that says the Dude will whip Butch."

Dandy Allen wiped his forehead with a handkerchief. "A thousand? Come off it, Will. We never bet more than five or ten dollars on these fights."

Uncle Will looked at the crowd and jeered. "Who is trying to hedge now?"

Laughter and shouts of derision were directed toward the gambler. Allen took it gracefully. "All right, Will, I'll cover that bet."

Butch Mears pulled a leather poke from his pocket. "I'd like to get some of that easy money, Will."

The crowd took up the cry of "Me too."

Uncle Will held up his arms for silence. "Just line up, folks. Judge Baker will get a pencil and paper and record all bets and hold the stakes."

A table and a chair were brought from the Whitehorse Saloon and placed on the wooden sidewalk. Judge Baker sat taking bets from the long line that formed.

Butch Mears pulled Uncle Will to one side. "What's the idear, Will? You want I should let this Dude whip me?"

"No, Butch, you just do your damnedest to win."

When all bets had been placed, Uncle Will ordered everybody off the street and onto the wooden sidewalks. Meanwhile he addressed the stranger. "I think it only fair to tell you that we fight a little different out here than you do back East. Everything goes. Nearest thing you have to it back East is what you call lumberjack fighting. I guess we are ready now. Let her rip, and may the best man win."

Uncle Will sat on the edge of the wooden sidewalk with Dandy Allen beside him. Allen covered his eyes with mock horror. "I can't bear to watch it, Will. The Dude will expect Butch to come in slugging. Butch will ram him instead."

Mears dove with great speed, for a man his size, at the Dude's stomach in an attempt to ram his opponent with his head. To the spectators it seemed as if the Dude was paralyzed with fright; but a split second before Mears reached him, he sidestepped, stuck out his foot, and tripped the mule driver. The crowd roared with laughter as Butch's nose plowed a furrow in the dirt.

Uncle Will slapped Allen on the back. "That will rile Butch and he'll go at the Dude swinging. Watch the Dude cut Butch's face to ribbons."

Mears charged the Dude with his hamlike fists slamming at the air, but his punches never seemed to land as the Dude kept him off balance with a steady tattoo of left jabs.

The Dude then feinted Mears into position and sunk a powerful left hook into the mule driver's stomach. Mears appeared to be unconscious although still on his feet. He stood with his arms hanging at his sides, with his right foot placed backward as if to keep himself from falling.

Dandy Allen rubbed his hands. "This is the end of your Dude, Will. Butch is setting him up to give your Dude the boot."

Uncle Will pulled his watch from his pocket. "I'll bet you a hundred dollars that within one minute Butch is sprawled flat on his back."

"I'll take that bet," Dandy answered.

The Dude stalked toward Mears with his right fist cocked as if for the final blow. Butch stood limply, with his arms hanging at his side, until the Dude was within striking distance of his foot. With a move so fast his leg seemed blurred, Mears aimed a kick at the Dude's chin.

The Dude jerked his head back just in time. His hands followed Butch's leg into the air, grasping it by toe and heel. The Dude whirled his own body around, twisting the foot as he did so. Butch was suspended in the air for a moment, and then hurled to the ground.

Uncle Will looked at his watch. "That's another hundred you owe me, Dandy. Exactly forty seconds." He returned the watch to his brocaded waistcoat.

Butch bounded to his feet. With a roar of rage he charged the Dude. The suddenness of the attack enabled him to wrap his big arms around the Dude's chest.

Dandy Allen smiled. "This is definitely the end of your Dude, Will. Butch will bust every rib in his body. You are the only man in the Territory that ever broke that hold."

"I've another hundred that says the Dude will break the hold, Dandy."

Allen shook his head. "Something tells me I'd be a fool to bet any more against the Dude, but I have to cover that bet."

The crowd held its breath as they watched the Dude force up his arms until his hands were cupped under the mule driver's chin. Slowly the Dude pushed back Butch's head. The interlocking wrist grip Butch had around the Dude was slowly pulled apart. In desperation Butch tried to knee the Dude, but the stranger had twisted his hips sideways. As the hold was broken, the Dude grabbed Mears by the wrist with a flying mare hold, and threw the mule driver over his head. Still holding Butch's wrist, he fell on top of him with his elbow crashing into his opponent's Adam's apple. The mule driver's body went limp. The Dude got to his feet, walked to where his clothes were piled, and began dressing.

Uncle Will slapped Dandy Allen on the back. "That will teach you to bet against a Fitzgerald."

"You mean—" Dandy, though his profession depended upon his being able to hide his feelings, could not restrain the surprise in his voice.

"I sure do, Dandy. Come on and meet my brother Tom. I used to be able to lick him, but I wouldn't want to try it now." He approached his brother. "Welcome to Silver-lode, Tom."

Tom grabbed his brother's outstretched hand. "Hello, Will." He nodded toward Butch Mears, who was being helped to his feet. "Why didn't you stop it, Will? You knew I could take him. Even John could take him."

Uncle Will laughed. "And pass up a golden opportunity to make a bet on a sure thing? No, Tom, I couldn't resist it."

Tom put on his coat and bowler hat. "You haven't changed a bit."

Uncle Will held up his arms and shouted to the crowd. "Boys, meet my brother, Tom Fitzgerald. And to celebrate the occasion, the drinks are on the house at the Whitehorse."

Tom waved a friendly greeting to the crowd, then walked over to Butch Mears and held out his hand. "Will you shake hands, Butch Mears?"

Mears smiled between bloody lips as he grasped the outstretched hand. "Ain't feeling so bad about losing now I know you're Will's brother. Before he came here, I could lick any man in the Territory. Now there's two of you. Glad to know you, Tom."

5

PAPA BUYS *THE SILVERLODE*
ADVOCATE

Aᴄᴛᴇʀ ᴀ ᴅʀɪɴᴋ in the Whitehorse Saloon, Uncle Will accompanied his brother to the Miner's Hotel, and waited until Tom had washed and changed clothes. When they returned to the Whitehorse, they went directly to the suite of rooms on the second floor where Queenie joined them at dinner served by a Chinese waiter. When the meal was over, Queenie discreetly withdrew.

Uncle Will handed his brother a cigar and held the candle on the table while it was lit. He leaned back in his chair, hooking his thumbs in the belt of his jeweled holster.

"Now, tell me, Tom, what brings you out to this God-forsaken country and how in the world did you find me?"

Tom had long ago made up his mind that he couldn't tell his brother of the death-bed promise. He exhaled a mouthful of smoke. "Mamma is dead," he said without any preliminary and then went on to describe her illness and passing away.

When he'd finished, Uncle Will shook his head. "I know I should feel something, but I don't. What's the matter with me anyway? You tell me Mother is dead and it's as if you told me a stranger had died."

Tom shrugged. "I really don't know unless it is as Father says and you are the lost one of this generation."

Uncle Will laughed scornfully. "Surely you don't believe in that legend of the curse."

Tom drummed his fingers on the table. "I don't know. I really don't know. There was Uncle Sean and all those others back for generations. And Will, you must have believed it yourself, or you wouldn't have left home."

Uncle Will took a brandy tumbler between the palms of his hands and began rolling the glass. "Poor Mamma. When I was a kid, I didn't really want to hurt her or Papa. But there was something inside me which seemed to rebel every time they told me not to do something. It was like a challenge to me and I just had to disobey. I never really felt free until I left home. This is the land of the six-shooter. After I killed my first man, I decided it was best never to write home again. I did have that much concern for Mamma and Papa. I didn't want to bring any disgrace to the family. I felt that my own life was to do with as I wished. It made it easier for me and easier for them. But enough about me, Tom. Why did you come here? I've always pictured you as stepping right into Papa's shoes."

Tom's eyes wandered around the luxuriously furnished apartment, from its Brussels carpet to the glass chandelier above the oak dining-room table. It was difficult for him to lie to his brother, but he knew he must.

"Ever since you left home, I've been reading a lot about the West. I felt it my duty to stay home as long as Mamma lived. With her death my obligation ceased. Papa is in good health. Josie is married. Catherine is a beautiful girl, and betrothed. John is a priest. I knew if I remained I would be only a reflection of what Papa wanted me to be. I wanted a chance to stand on my own feet and make my

own life. I told Papa how I felt and he advanced me a part
of my inheritance. I came out West. I've been traveling
around looking for a newspaper I could buy. In Salt Lake
City I met a William C. Dunbar, business manager of *The
Herald*. He explained to me that all newspapers in Utah
Territory were either anti- or pro-Mormon and it wasn't
profitable to attempt to publish an independent newspaper.
He named several editors who had tried and failed. Among
the newspapers mentioned was *The Silverlode Advocate*. He
told me that it had operated as an independent for two years;
then had to change to anti-Mormon. He got me a copy and
I couldn't believe my eyes when I saw your name on it as
publisher." Tom did not tell his brother that he'd gone to
talk to Dunbar after his visit with Father Farley.

Uncle Will threw back his head and began to laugh.
"That isn't what happened at all," he said, then explained
how he'd acquired *The Advocate* and the reason for the
change in editorial policy. "However," he concluded, "you
couldn't pick a poorer place in the whole country to buy a
newspaper, Tom. They say that Ogden is 'the graveyard of
Western Journalism,' and I've heard Salt Lake City called
'Journalistic Cemetery.' You just can't win. You are damned
if you do and damned if you don't. If your editorial policy
is against the Mormons, they'll boycott the paper as they
are now doing to *The Advocate*. If your editorial policy is in
favor of the Mormons, the Gentiles will call you a Jack Mormon, and not only boycott you, but wreck your office and
beat you up. It's happened to hundreds of editors and pub-
lishers. And you can't sit on the fence. It's been tried by
dozens of newspapers and they all failed."

Tom thought for a moment. "But according to Mr. Dunbar, *The Silverlode Advocate* was an independent and operated that way for two years."

"It was a little different here, Tom. In the first place all the Gentiles realized that if the Mormons stopped trading with us, we would be forced to bring in food and supplies all the way from Salt Lake City. And in the second place, Dave Powell happens to be a man you instinctively like. Once in a while some drunken miner used to beat Dave up, but we discouraged that by having Butch Mears or some-one else beat the tar out of the miner."

Tom removed the cigar from his mouth and laid it on a brass ashtray. He cupped his hands together and rested his elbows on the linen tablecloth. "Sell me *The Advocate,* Will. You say Dave Powell made a living with it. I'm certain I can. I have part of my inheritance in the Walker Bank in Salt Lake. I have never asked you a favor, Will. Do this one for me."

Uncle Will shook his head. "This is a tough country. It needs a lot of taming and civilizing. Life is cheap here and a man must fight for his life. I've killed eight men since coming West. I admit there's a need for men like you here, but all men must stand on their own feet. If I knew a man was going to kill you in a fair and square gun fight, I wouldn't interfere. I'd have to let him kill you. I'd kill him later, but I couldn't prevent him from killing you. That is our code out here, and you live and you die by it."

Tom nodded his head. "I would not have it any other way."

Uncle Will leaned back in his chair. "There is more. I promised Dave he'd have a job for as long as he wanted. *The Advocate,* even if you got its circulation and advertising back to where Dave once had it, couldn't support you both."

Tom leaned forward and spoke forcefully. "I'll keep Powell on as my typesetter and assistant. I don't want to make a lot of money. I don't expect to make a lot of money.

I just want the opportunity to do something on my own. To be an individual. To stand on my own two feet. I will never ask your help financially or otherwise. Don't you understand, Will? This is what I came out West for. A newspaper and a good fight."

Uncle Will turned sidewise and stretched his long legs. He studied the toes of his highly polished boots for a moment. "You didn't ask about Queenie. You must have guessed she is my mistress."

Tom pushed back the cowlick of hair. "I came West to live my own life and not yours, Will."

Uncle Will looked across the table into his brother's eyes. "Always remember that, Tom. I didn't travel thousands of miles to get away from Papa's and Mamma's preaching, only to have you take their place. I don't honestly know if you can make the grade out here or not. We are an uncivilized, unprincipled, immoral and irreligious people, not counting the Mormons. The one thing we cherish most is our individual freedom to live any kind of life we choose and if we choose the road to Hell, we don't want anybody trying to save us. You try to live another man's life in this country, Tom, and he'll take yours. You try to reform one man or one woman, and even if you succeed, all other men and women will hate you for it."

Tom leaned back in his chair. "I could not succeed as a journalist if I were not objective and impartial. I know you are telling me indirectly that my Catholicism may lead me to speak out against the morals and manners of men. But this I will not do. I firmly believe that to separate the fourth estate from religion is just as important as separating religion from government."

Uncle Will shrugged. "All right, Tom, you can have *The Advocate* on condition you keep Dave Powell. And knowing you will insist on paying for it, I'll sell it to you for what I bet against it when I won it, two thousand dollars."

The next day Tom got Dave Powell sobered up and made arrangements to pay him ten dollars a week, plus board and room at Ma Burke's Boarding House. They were seated in the office of *The Advocate*.

"I'll accept your generous offer, Tom," Powell said, "at least until we get *The Advocate* back where I had it before I lost it. There really isn't enough money in it to support two people. Paper is our big problem. You just can't seem to get enough paper. I've set up a crude mill to produce paper from rags when I can get rags, and it's usually so dark you can barely read the print. Abe Glassman, the owner of the Emporium, has been a lifesaver many times. He keeps an extra stock of wrapping paper on hand. You might get some help from Granny. That is what we journalists in the Territory call *The Deseret News* in Salt Lake City. I wouldn't bank on it, though. Later, you can ask Bishop Aden to help you. He got paper for me many times when half the newspapers in the Territory couldn't go to press due to the shortage."

The first edition of *The Silverlode Advocate* under Tom's management was distributed free to homes in Adenville and free copies left in business establishments in Silverlode. In a boxed announcement on the first page, readers were in-

formed that beginning with the next issue the price of subscriptions would be five dollars per year, or twenty-five cents
per single copy. Advertising rates would be the same as those
prevailing when Dave Powell was publisher. Printing would
be quoted upon submission of requirements. The announcement attracted little attention; but the editorial in the first
edition caused a great deal of discussion.

From the editorial page of the March 21, 1884 edition of
The Silverlode Advocate, *Tom D. Fitzgerald, editor and
publisher.*

A CHANGE IN EDITORIAL POLICY

Your new editor received his training as a journalist from his
father who was also an editor, publisher and owner of a newspaper. Each morning when your editor reported for work his
father would make him read the following creed which was suspended in a wooden frame above his father's roll-top desk.

"A journalist who prints only the good about a person, issue,
thing, belief or political party is just as much a disgrace to his
profession as a journalist who prints only the bad about a person, issue, thing, belief or political party. It is not the duty of
a true journalist to defend or condemn the acts or morals of
men and governments. The true journalist is the voice of the
unbiased observer who presents only the facts. The true journalist does not shape the thinking of the people; but only presents the facts so the people may decide the issues themselves.
When he omits a single fact, either pro or con, he ceases to be
a true journalist."

This creed shall dictate the editorial policy of this newspaper
for as long as your editor is the publisher. Your editor believes
he has no more right to tell you what church you should attend

than he has to tell you how to vote. Let it be enough that a
man worships God, and the manner in which he manifests that
love for God be of his own choosing.

Editorially yours,
Tom D. Fitzgerald

Tom had three callers in his office two days after the editorial appeared. Bishop Aden, wearing his homespun suit
and black hat, was spokesman for the trio. He introduced
himself and then presented County Sheriff Hank Jeffers and
County Judge Potter. He remained standing, pulling at the
stubby lobe of his partially shot-off ear. His bluish gray eyes
seemed to probe into Tom's innermost soul.

"We Saints," the Bishop said, "have read the editorial in
The Advocate. We have come to look into the eyes of the
man who wrote it. We have come to look upon the face of
the man who wrote it. There were the doubters who did not
believe the man who wrote the editorial could be the brother
of Will Fitzgerald. There were the skeptics who scented in
the editorial some sort of a trick. There were more, like
myself, who upon reading the editorial felt it could have
been written only by a sincere man. I have looked into your
eyes, Tom Fitzgerald, and find them bright with honesty.
I have looked upon your face, Tom Fitzgerald, and find it
unfeigned. I have misjudged very few men in my life."

He placed his hand in his inside coat pocket and pulled
out a large envelope which he laid on the desk. "This envelope contains the names of six hundred residents of Adenville and a check drawn upon the Walker Bank in Salt Lake
City in the amount of three thousand dollars in payment
for one year's subscription to *The Advocate*. We shall re-

sume our advertising and send you our printing. We shall arrange for the relaying of important news to you from Salt Lake City over the church telegraph lines. And that concludes our mission here. We bid you good day, Tom Fitzgerald."

Tom held out his hands in a helpless gesture. "I find it hard to speak. I am overwhelmed. I'm doing this badly, I know, but permit me to thank you personally, Bishop Aden, and the good people of Adenville. I can only assure you that you haven't misjudged me."

After the Mormons had left, he sat at his desk staring with unseeing eyes. He tried in vain to reconcile the first Latter-Day Saints he'd met personally with the far-fetched stories he'd heard about them. He could not conceive of anything more diametrically opposed than associating the gaunt, homely faced Bishop with lascivious conduct. Was not this man with eyes that seemed to probe into a man's heart living proof that the polygamous tenet in the Latter-Day Saint religion was dictated by the law of supply and demand, rather than lustfulness? Did not every religion go through its baptism of ridicule and persecution before it became indestructible? Did one false tenet of a religion make it a false religion? Were not some of the tenets of all religions discarded in the fullness of time? Surely, this Bishop with his homely, gentle face could not by any stretch of the imagination be considered a sinful man. Tom found himself completely bewildered by his first personal contact with the Mormons.

His reputation as a journalist grew with each succeeding issue of *The Advocate*. The only thing that could be construed as anti-Mormon were the lists of names of Latter-Day Saints who were arrested for polygamy, and the results of their trials and imprisonment. He considered this factual news. The Saints did not try to dissuade him from printing these lists because often it was their first indication that a relative in another part of the Territory had been arrested.

There were many among the Gentiles who might have found fault with his editorial policy; but none dared call him a Jack Mormon, knowing he had beaten Butch Mears. There were a few who might have goaded him into a gun fight, but they held back this urge because they knew they in turn would have had to face the guns of Will Fitzgerald.

6

PAPA MEETS MAMMA

Tom's first printing job was new menus for the Erin Cafe when it changed hands. The Canton Cafe became the Erin Cafe and the transfer of ownership from Lee Wong to Bridget O'Flynn was accomplished without a single dollar being exchanged or any papers being signed.

Bridget O'Flynn, who after her arrival in this country had followed the railroad westward by working in railway beaneries and hash houses, came to Silverlode on a stagecoach that groaned under her massive weight. She was a woman of indeterminate age, with a round face sprinkled with freckles, a button nose and fiery red hair which she wore in a chignon at the nape of her neck. She obtained a job as a waitress in the Canton Cafe because her time of entering the place had been very opportune—she'd arrived just as two drunken miners were about to cut off Lee Wong's pigtail. Bridget waded into the two miners, swinging her hamlike fists like a man and asking no quarter. In a matter of minutes the miners found themselves thrown into Corry Street like sacks of wheat.

Bridget worked in the Canton Cafe for a few months. At least once a week some inebriated miner got fresh with her and ended up being thrown into the street. There was even some heated discussion around the campfires at the camp ground as to whether Bridget could lick Butch Mears.

One night Bridget entered the Whitehorse Saloon with her clothes in disarray and claimed Lee Wong had attempted to attack her. The Chinaman escaped from Silverlode one jump ahead of a mob bent on lynching him. Regarding the incident, Tom wrote in *The Advocate:*

CANTON CAFE CHANGES HANDS

Our readers are familiar with the story of how the Canton Cafe became the Erin Cafe. In the interests of impartial reporting your editor would like to recall an incident that took place the day before the Cafe changed hands. Webb Miller, who stands over six feet and weighs over two hundred pounds, was feeling the results of several hours of drinking in the Fairplay Saloon. He thought he'd have a little fun with Bridget O'Flynn and got fresh with her. Bridget knocked Webb off the stool upon which he was sitting in the Cafe and then tossed him right through the plate-glass window. Lee Wong was about five feet two inches in height and weighed not more than one hundred and ten pounds. Your editor isn't casting any doubt upon the veracity of Bridget's claim that Wong attempted to attack her, because as Bridget herself said, "Sure, and if the heathen wasn't guilty, he would have stayed and let the boys string him up."

Tom wasn't a drinking or a gambling man. He found relaxation in visiting the camp grounds every evening, where he participated in the wrestling matches, foot races and weight-lifting contests. He sat around campfires and listened to tall tales of the West, or debated issues ranging all the way from politics to horse trading. He found pleasure in joining in the songs which were generally sung to the accompaniment of a banjo. Sometimes he'd listen to the traveling evangelists who made the camp ground their pulpits.

His first meeting with Doc Tethers was the result of a bad slide at the Silverlode Mine. Dale Ferrin, the mine superintendent, came by *The Advocate* office to tell him of the accident. "I'm on my way to find Doc Tethers," Ferrin said. "I hope he's sober."

Tom walked across Whiskey Row and entered the Whitehorse Saloon with the mine superintendent. They saw Doc Tethers standing at the bar drinking, with the big hunchback watching him. Ferrin approached Tethers. "Doc, there's been a bad slide at the Silverlode. Five men hurt. Three of them in very bad shape. You've got to help them, Doc."

Doc Tethers did not even turn his head. "My dear sir," he said, "I am not an employee of the Silverlode Mining and Development Corporation. There is no shingle on my office soliciting patients. I did not travel across a continent to administer to the health and well-being of a group of moronic miners. My sole purpose in coming to Silverlode was to drink myself to death, and you, sir, are interfering with that purpose. I bid you good day."

Ferrin shrugged. "I was hoping you'd be sober, Doc."

Tom grabbed Tethers' arm and spun him around. "You call yourself a doctor. What of your Hippocratic Oath?"

Tom found himself suddenly seized in the hairy arms of the giant hunchback from whose throat low guttural growls were coming. The hunchback picked him off the floor and began shaking him like a baby.

Doc Tethers pointed at the floor. "Put him down, Peter," he said gently. As the hunchback released Tom, Doc Tethers again became cold. "You, sir, are suffering under a misapprehension. I renounced the medical profession and my Hippocratic Oath many years ago. Now, if you gentlemen don't mind, I shall resume my drinking which you so rudely interrupted."

Tom accompanied Ferrin back to the mine. "All we can hope for," Ferrin said, "is that the men will live until Doc is sober in the morning. If there is any doctor in the world who can save a life, it's Doc Tethers when he's sober. He must have been one of the most brilliant surgeons in the world before whatever it was that made him come to Silverlode. The man has breeding and culture, but he just seems to hate the entire human race when he's drinking."

"Is he the only doctor in Silverlode?" Tom asked.

"Most of the time," Ferrin nodded. "We can't get a good doctor to stay here. When we do get a doctor, the first man he loses makes it tough for him. All the man's friends blame the doctor and tell him that Doc Tethers could have saved their friend. There have been many times when men were seriously injured and refused to let the Mine doctor even examine them, saying they'd wait until Doc Tethers got sober. The trouble is that the only time Doc is ever sober is in the morning. He sleeps late, but as soon as he is awake he heads for a saloon and starts drinking."

Tom shook his head. "I wonder what made him like that."

Ferrin shrugged. "I can only guess that the hunchback has something to do with it. Every time Doc gets drunk he starts damning every member of the human race who has a straight back and a normal mind."

As Tom became acquainted with the citizens of Silverlode, he found himself dropping into the Emporium more and more often to talk with Abe Glassman. The little Jew was a well-read man and they discussed the arts, sciences and philosophy. Tom learned a great deal of the Jewish religion, which engendered in him a great compassion for a people decimated and persecuted, driven from country to country.

"This America shall be your people's permanent home," he said one night. "Spain flourished until the Jews were driven from it. Then, Spain began to decay. Holland gained by this persecution because many of the Jews driven from Spain migrated there. Holland became prosperous. It is history, Abe, that wherever your people are permitted to live, prosperity follows. I firmly believe that at last your people have found a home in this great country."

Abe Glassman nodded his head, which was covered with a skull cap. "It will be so, only because of men like you."

After getting to know his neighbors, Tom took a realistic view of his prospects. He knew that *The Advocate* could not support himself and Dave Powell. He was attending a church social at the Mormon Tabernacle in his capacity as journalist one evening and spoke of this to Bishop Aden. The Bishop suggested he seek additional subscriptions in nearby Mormon communities.

Tom hired a one-horse rig from Tanner's Livery Stable the following Monday. He followed the road along the base of the plateau northward. The rugged beauty of the country fascinated him. The green branches of the gnarled cedar trees looked like umbrellas. The arms of the joshua trees extended upward as if in prayer. White sego lilies and Indian paint brush decorated the desert-land. The sagebrush seemed purple from a distance. Tamimump, which the Indians used for tobacco, grew among the greasewood. The crimson sandstone and chalk-white cliffs towered above him.

At the top of a small hill he pulled the horse to a stop and had his first look at the town of Enoch. The sight of green trees lining the streets, the orchards, vineyards, gardens and green fields presented an exaggerated contrast to the desert-land around it. He could see a portion of the man-made canal with willows growing along its bank which carried the water that had made the desert bloom.

The main thoroughfare of Enoch had ditches with running water on each side providing moisture for the cotton-wood, mulberry and poplar trees which lined the street. Places of business were between dwelling houses, except for one block on one side of the street. Here a barber shop and saddlery stood on each side of Neilsen's Mercantile Store.

Tom drew the horse to a stop in front of the store and tied the reins to the hitching rack. He knocked the dust from his clothes with his wide-brimmed hat as he looked in the windows of the store. The owner had tried to put as much diversified material in the window as possible. A ging-ham sunbonnet was separated from a bolt of dress goods by a cowbell. Shoes and ladies' corsets were displayed beside dishes, pots and pans. Blankets for horses and for human beings were piled on top of each other.

Tom entered the store. Two elderly men were seated on empty boxes playing checkers near a big iron stove, so intent on their game that they didn't raise their heads. Along one side of the store a red-grained counter guarded shelves piled high with bolts of dress materials, shoes, boots, parasols, purses, shawls, ladies' hats and sunbonnets. Men's hats, shirts, work gloves filled two shelves. Boxes of Mormon underwear called garments, worn only by those Saints who had been married in the Temple in Salt Lake City or who had been on a mission, occupied one whole section.

Near the entrance to the store stood a shelved glass showcase stuffed with men's celluloid collars, cuffs, shoe laces, shaving mugs, straight razors, hat pins, fans, combs, beads, kid curlers, curling irons, buttons and corset stays. A wooden case of Kerr's cotton spool thread and a case of Diamond Dye stood on the counter in the center.

On the opposite side of the store was a counter with glass compartments filled with beans, meal, sugar, spices, salt, rice; and, incongruously, pills, patent medicines, horehound drops, licorice, lemon drops, rock candy, peppermint sticks and cookies. A big iron coffee grinder painted red stood on the counter next to a smaller counter containing more pat- ent medicines, knives, forks, pocket knives, hunting knives and some blue fluted glassware. Behind the counter on the wall there hung from pegs, horse collars, lanterns, cartridge belts, guns, pails, kerosene lamps, bridles and shovels.

The Post Office was at the rear of the store with a seed counter on one side and a door leading to the storeroom in the rear of the building.

Tom saw none of these things. He saw only a girl standing on a stepladder behind the counter placing goods on a shelf. Her long corn-colored hair hung in two thick waist-length braids. Her hazel eyes showed curiosity as she saw the stran- ger, and her small mouth crinkled into a smile producing two dimples in her cheeks. She descended from the ladder and stood with her head cocked slightly to one side as if lis- tening to something only she could hear.

"May I help you, sir?" she asked.

Tom tried to speak, but his tongue clove to the roof of his mouth. He was embarrassed by his rudeness in staring, but could not restrain himself. He felt dizzy as the blood rushed to his face. He was looking at the one girl in this world his mother had often told him he would some day meet.

Concern flickered across the delicate beauty of her face. "Are you ill, sir? Can I get you a glass of water?"

Tom heard and felt his breath rasp in his throat. Ill? He was definitely ill. As ill as the first cigar he'd ever smoked had made him. As ill as the first drink of whiskey he'd ever drank had made him. He could see no possible similarity between the cigar and the whiskey and love at first sight, but it was the way he felt.

He had often rehearsed what he would say when he finally met the one girl in the world for him. He would doff his hat and bow with old-world gallantry. He would smile gently at her. He would take her dainty hand and press it to his lips. He would be a dashing cavalier whose sweet words of adoration would sweep her off her feet.

But he did none of these things. He stood there like a tongue-tied schoolboy. What a spectacle he was making of himself! What a humiliating thing to happen! He turned and ran from the store, climbed into the rig and galloped the horse out of town until he came to where the farmland abutted the desert-land. There he sat for more than an hour trying to compose himself. When he returned to town he was determined that it would be as he'd always planned it to be.

The two old men were still playing checkers as he reentered the store. The girl was still behind the counter. She seemed surprised to see him again and a little hesitant.

Tom took a deep breath, removed his hat and bowed gracefully. "May I introduce myself. Tom Fitzgerald, Esquire, your obedient servant."

The two old men playing checkers interrupted their game and stared at the maker of flowery speeches.

The girl blushed momentarily. "Your name," she said in

a low sweet voice, "is vaguely familiar to me. I have heard it; but cannot recall where or when."

Tom laid his hat on the counter next to the big cheese which was covered with cheesecloth. "It is the name of a man who knows you well. It is the name of a man who has met you many times in his dreams. It is the name of a man who has carried a picture of your dear face in his heart since the days of his youth. It is the name of a man who begs with all humility for the honor of calling upon you and paying his respects to your family."

The girl seemed a little frightened as she moved hesitantly toward the beaded curtains. "You are joshing me, sir. I'd better call my father."

"By all means, please do."

Sweyn Neilsen parted the curtains with an umbrella. He had got the bumbershoot habit in England, and his gold-handled umbrella was as much a part of his dress as his pants. He used it as a cane when walking. He used it to point out merchandise in the store to his customers. He used it to tap on the floor to emphasize points when arguing. He hooked it in the crook of his arm while wrapping up packages.

He shifted the umbrella to the crook of his arm and held out his hand. "I have heard of you, Tom Fitzgerald, and on occasion read your newspaper. I am Sweyn Neilsen."

Tom shook hands. "I am very glad to know you, sir, and I congratulate you upon being the father of such a beautiful and charming daughter."

Sweyn Neilsen backed up a few feet and pointed his umbrella at Tom. "You speak gibberish. State your business with me, young man."

"Certainly, sir," Tom said. "Bishop Aden of Adenville suggested that I contact you with a view of increasing the circulation of my newspaper. I have free copies in the rig outside with subscription blanks. I would like to arrange for you to become my agent in Enoch. I would, of course, make a financial arrangement with you to pay you for your time."

"There will be no need of that," Sewyn Neilsen replied. "I have read your newspaper and know you to be a friend of us Latter-Day Saints. I shall be pleased to act as your agent as long as your newspaper retains its present editorial policy. I shall also introduce you to Bishop Trainor, who will make arrangements to send our printing to you instead of to Salt Lake City. The entire arrangement was thoroughly discussed with Bishop Aden some time ago."

Tom grinned. "That is most generous of you, sir. And now as to my own personal qualifications. I can furnish excellent references as to my character, reputation, family background, citizenship and financial rating."

Sweyn Neilsen rubbed his chin whiskers with the handle of his umbrella as a puzzled look etched his face. "That isn't necessary. I have said I would act as your agent."

"You misunderstand me, sir," Tom smiled. "I made this latter statement as a prelude to requesting your permission to call upon your daughter."

Sweyn Neilsen raised his umbrella and pointed it at the brash young man. "I am afraid that the sight of a pretty face has temporarily destroyed your power to reason. I suggest that you return to Silverlode and give your mind time to orient itself so you can rationalize. My daughter is a God-fearing believer in the tenets of the Church of Jesus Christ of Latter-Day Saints. I am confident that after you have given yourself time to think this over, you'll realize how impossible your request is."

Tom nodded slowly. "I'll do as you suggest, sir, but even

so, I know I shall be back." He left the store and after feed-ing and watering his horse at the livery stable, began the drive back to Silverlode. As he drove through the vast ex-panse of the desert with the silence broken only by the clop-ping of the horse's hoofs, Tom Fitzgerald communed with his conscience, his heart, his very soul.

The next morning after a hurried breakfast in the Miner's Cafe, he stopped at the Emporium and bought a box of chocolates. He crossed Whiskey Row to Tanner's Livery Stable and rented the best buggy available and a team of bay horses. He stopped once during the drive to Enoch to pick some wild flowers. He left the team and buggy at the livery stable, knocked the dust from his clothes and received per-mission to wash up in the livery stable owner's home.

He was probably the best dressed man ever to enter the town of Enoch, with his striped pants tucked neatly into polished boots, a frock coat unbuttoned to reveal a check-ered vest across which hung a heavy gold watch chain, a high wing collar with a bright red ascot; and he wore a black beaver hat.

The two old men playing checkers had been joined by a dog which lay stretched beneath the pot-bellied stove. They all three watched expectantly as Tom walked to the counter and looked across it into the eyes of Tena Neilsen.

He doffed his hat and laid it on the counter, placed the box of chocolates beside his hat, and held out the bunch of wild flowers toward her. "I am distressed that I must speak to you this way, in public," he said earnestly, "but your father has refused me permission to call on you in your home. I don't even know your name, and yet I've carried the image of your pretty face engraven upon my heart for years. Please, please tell me your name."

One of the checker players slapped his knee. "Well, I'll

be dad-burned. In all my born days I never seed anything so golly."

Tena Neilsen took the flowers and laid them on the counter. She felt bewildered and a little frightened at the attention this handsome stranger was paying her. "My name is Tena, Tena Neilsen."

"Tena," Tom repeated it like a caress. "A sweet name. A beautiful name. A dear name. I shall devote my every moment toward the day when you grant me permission to call you Miss Tena."

One of the checker players disappeared behind the curtains at the rear of the store. Sweyn Neilsen came into the store swinging his umbrella in the air as he pointed it toward his daughter. "Tena, go home this instant!"

She started to pick up her gifts, but her father shouted; "Leave the candy and flowers, daughter."

After a shy smile toward Tom Fitzgerald, she reluctantly walked toward the rear of the store.

Sweyn Neilsen grasped the umbrella and pounded it on the floor with every word he spoke. "Mister Fitzgerald, I assumed that you were an intelligent man. Mister Fitzgerald, I assumed that you were a reasonable man. Mister Fitzgerald, I assumed that you were not an idiot. I see now I was wrong. I shall, therefore, make it plain enough for even a dolt to understand. Leave my store immediately. Don't ever attempt to see my daughter again or you will answer to me personally."

Tom put on his hat. His face grew grim with resolve. "I shall give up my courtship of your daughter, sir, only when she herself spurns my attentions. This may be hard for you to comprehend, sir, but I am in love with her and I not only intend to make that love known to her; but also seek her hand in marriage, with or without your permission. I did not wait these many years for the one girl in the world for me, only to have you by a few words take her from me. Now, good day, sir."

That afternoon neighbors near the Neilsen home were treated to a strange sight. A handsome stranger leaned on the whitewashed picket fence and stared at an upstairs bedroom window they knew to be Tena's.

When Sweyn Neilsen heard about it, he sent an urgent message to Bishop Trainor. They held a long conference in the rear of the store.

At precisely six o'clock that evening, Tom opened the gate and walked boldly up to the front door of the Neilsen home. Sweyn Neilsen, who had arrived home by the back door an hour before, opened the front door.

Tom removed his hat. "I present myself as an uninvited guest for supper, sir. I know it to be one of your religious customs always to set an extra plate for any unexpected guest."

Sweyn Neilsen shrugged. "I feel you take unfair advantage of me; but I abide by our customs."

Tom entered the parlor. He walked across a homemade rag rug with straw matting and seated himself on a Victorian horsehair chair covered with decorative red plush buttons. Unable to meet the stare of his unwilling host, his eyes wandered over the room. The walls of the parlor were adorned with large pictures of family ancestors in deep, gilt-edged frames.

Finally Sweyn Neilsen, who was sitting in a rocking chair, spoke. "You are a stubborn man, Tom Fitzgerald. I cannot break with custom and refuse you supper; but I can deny you the privilege of having my daughter dine with you. After we have eaten, I shall prove the utter futility and ridiculousness of your actions."

The heavy green and red curtains between the parlor and dining room parted. Elizabeth Neilsen, Tena's mother, entered and was introduced. She was a small woman with dimpled cheeks who moved with grace and poise. Her hair attracted Tom's attention. It was dark brown and exceedingly neat and well groomed.

Elizabeth Neilsen smiled. "Yes, young man, it is a wig. I lost all my hair from fever while crossing the plains." She turned to her husband. "Supper is ready."

Amazed at the unembarrassed frankness of the woman, Tom could only stammer, "Your eyes, they are like your daughter's, Madam."

He followed them into the dining room. A large oak table was set with willow-ware dishes upon a homemade tablecloth. A matching oak sideboard with a mirror held cut-glass dishes. He waited until Elizabeth Neilsen was seated and then sat down on one of the leather-backed chairs. He bowed his head as Sweyn Neilsen asked the blessing.

Despite his embarrassment, Tom took a second helping of stewed chicken, dumplings and mashed potatoes. The hot homemade bread spread with honey melted in his mouth. There was homemade apple pie for dessert. A pitcher of cold milk was the only beverage; the Mormons never drank tea or coffee.

Elizabeth Neilsen tried to make conversation several times during the supper, but her husband's meaningful looks soon made her lapse into silence. When the meal was over, Tom followed his host into the parlor. He almost lit a cigar before remembering that the Mormons never smoked. He sat down in the same Victorian chair.

Without his umbrella Sweyn Neilsen seemed not to know what to do with his hands. He finally folded them across his chest as he leaned against the fireplace. "Bishop Trainor and his son Mark will be here soon. I have gone to extreme lengths to prove to you that your actions are not only futile; but also not in keeping with the opinion we Saints have of your sense of justice and decency."

He had just finished speaking when there was a knock at the door. He opened it to admit Bishop Trainor and his son Mark, a boy of nineteen.

After being introduced and shaking hands, Bishop Trainor clasped his hands behind his back. "We know you to be an honest man, Tom Fitzgerald. We know you to be an honorable man. We know you to be a man of good morals. We know you to be a just man. We trust you to do the right thing when you are in complete possession of the facts in this case. The facts are these: my son Mark and Tena Neilsen have been sweethearts since childhood. They are betrothed and will marry in the fall when Tena is eighteen. It is a fitting and proper marriage between two people of the same religious faith, the same customs, the same habits, the same environment. We ask you as an honorable man to do nothing to jeopardize the happiness of these two persons and the tranquillity of our community. We realize that it would be possible for a handsome man like yourself to perhaps turn the head of a mere girl, but we trust to your sense of honor not to do so."

Tom seemed crestfallen. "I must hear it from her own lips. I must be certain that it is hopeless."

"Very well," Sweyn Neilsen agreed.

Tena couldn't understand why all the fuss about the handsome stranger. When her father had brought Bishop

Trainor secretly in the back way that afternoon while the stranger had stood at the picket fence in front of the house, she'd wondered why they considered it so important. Bishop Trainor had spoken eloquently to her. "We cannot afford to antagonize this man," he concluded. "He can do us Saints considerable harm in his newspaper if he so desires. This makes it imperative that we do nothing to incur his enmity."

Tena truthfully assured her father and the Bishop that her only emotion upon seeing Tom Fitzgerald had been a mixture of curiosity and feminine pleasure in being so complimented. She did not tell her father or the Bishop that she had peeked from the bedroom window several times during the afternoon just to look at the handsome man. She did not understand what made her do so, other than a woman's curiosity.

That evening her father came to her room. "Tom Fitzgerald is in the parlor, daughter," he said very seriously. "He will not leave until you speak to him. I want you to tell him that you are betrothed to Mark and will marry him in the fall."

"But Father, I am not betrothed to Mark. I like him. I even love him. But as a sister loves a brother."

"That is nonsense, daughter. You and Mark have been in love since you were children. He is a fine young man. You will marry him upon reaching your eighteenth birthday. We will discuss that later. At present we are confronted with a very serious situation. You will tell this Tom Fitzgerald that you are betrothed to Mark and will marry Mark in the fall. You will do this at the urging of your father and your Bishop."

When Tena looked across the parlor into the eyes of Tom Fitzgerald, it seemed that for a moment they were alone in the room. For the first time in her life she was looking at a man and feeling herself a woman. As his eyes pleaded with her, she experienced an uncontrollable elation that her face was beautiful and her body desirable.

Her father's voice seemed far off. "My daughter, please tell this gentleman that you are betrothed to Mark and will marry him in the fall."

Her father and the Bishop expected her to tell a lie. She found it suddenly very hard to do. She dropped her head. "I am betrothed to Mark and will marry him in the fall." She spoke the words mechanically. She raised her head as she heard Tom Fitzgerald groan as if in pain. She watched him pluck his hat from the elkhorn hatrack. He turned and looked at her with such anguish distorting his handsome features that she had a wild impulse to run to him, push back the cowlick of hair and touch his face.

"All is lost," he cried out dramatically. "I find myself suddenly, and irrevocably, without anything for which to live." He bowed and with sagging shoulders went through the doorway.

7

THE SETTLEMENT OF ENOCH

My maternal great-grandfather, Christopher Neilsen, claimed to be a descendant of Harold Bluetooth, the first Christian King of Denmark. He was an extremist in all things. His love of the land made him a tyrant with his tenant families; his love of country made him an enemy of all other nationalities; his devotion to his Lutheran faith made him intolerant of all other religions.

His eldest son, Christopher IV, he molded in his own image and after a proper education began teaching his son to prepare for the day the boy would take over the stewardship of the estate. His second eldest son, Harold, he sent to Vienna to study to become a physician and surgeon. His youngest son, Sweyn, he sent to England to become a barrister in preparation for the day the boy would enter the diplomatic service of his country.

Grandpa Sweyn's destiny was shaped by three religions: Lutheran, Episcopalian and Mormon. He met and fell in love with Elizabeth Fairgate, an Episcopalian, while studying in England, and married her in 1864 before completing his education. When his father received word that Sweyn had married an Englishwoman and not a Lutheran, he promptly disowned, disinherited and forbade his son ever to return to the ancestral home.

This harsh edict was somewhat mitigated by a letter Grandpa Sweyn received from his two brothers, which read in part:

"Since you have made this decision to cast your lot with a nation of shopkeepers, we are enclosing a bank draft to make this possible. We do this only at Mother's request and without Father's knowledge."

It was perhaps the insolence of the letter that influenced Grandpa Sweyn to abide by it. He knew there wasn't enough money to complete his education and support himself and his wife. This was a period when all religions bordered on fanaticism. His wife had lost her parents when a child during an epidemic, and had been raised by an uncle and aunt who believed that anyone who wasn't an Episcopalian was an infidel. When she married a Lutheran, they promptly disowned her.

Grandpa Sweyn became a shopkeeper, opening a bakery that specialized in Danish pastry. With the help of a Danish baker he hired, he managed to make a living. He made his home in four rooms above the bakery shop.

The intolerance of his own family and that of his wife drove him almost to the brink of agnosticism. For four years he attended no church and said no prayers. During this time, his wife had two children whom they named Tena and Sena. The coming of the children began to affect his business. People began making pointed remarks about rearing Godless children.

Destiny guided his footsteps into a park one Sunday. While his wife watched the children, Grandpa Sweyn joined a crowd who were listening to a Mormon missionary. The

fiery zeal, the sincere enthusiasm, the complete impervious-
ness of the missionary to the sneering epithets, jibes and
deprecating remarks of the hostile crowd made a deep impression on Grandpa Sweyn. He was one of the very few who
accepted some tracts the missionary passed out when he'd
finished speaking.

Grandpa Sweyn read the tracts during the week, and the
following Sunday again went to the park to listen to the
missionary. When the missionary had concluded his sermon,
Grandpa invited him to his home. In the small parlor above
the bakery the missionary extolled the Latter-Day Saints
faith to Grandpa and Grandma Neilsen. He became a regu-
lar visitor. As Grandpa Sweyn listened, he knew that he'd
been trying too long to dam up the universal longing of
man to worship God. One night he dropped to his knees
and cried out to God for forgiveness. As his confession
poured from his lips, an unseen clenched fist around his
heart seemed to relax its grip and a blinding light drove the
darkness from his mind. He felt his wife's hand in his. They
had found the way.

Two days later they were baptized and confirmed as Latter-
Day Saints. A month later Grandpa Sweyn sold his bakery
shop. His name with his family's appeared in the *Millennial
Star,* the Latter-Day Saints' European newspaper, as being
among several hundred converts sailing for the United States
on a chartered packet ship. They traveled by train from
New York City to Benton, Wyoming, from where they made
the journey to the Great Basin in a covered wagon caravan.

In later years when asked about the trip across the plains,
Grandpa Sweyn would shake his head and say, "It wasn't
easy or very comfortable." One excerpt from his diary indi-
cates this was quite an understatement.

"It seems that everybody is hungry, ill or dying. The children cry out for food. The women stifle their sobs. The men choke back their tears. My little girls must walk because my wagon is filled with the sick and the dying. My good wife lies desperately ill with fever. We halt every now and then to separate the dead from the living and give the departed a hasty burial. Each time we stop I pray that God has spared my wife. As we bury our dead their places are taken immediately by those too ill to walk. Merciful God, I beseech thee for strength for my wife, continued health for my children, and courage for myself and the brothers and sisters of this wagon train, that we may survive this journey and find the peace we seek in Zion."

When Grandma Elizabeth left Benton, Wyoming, she had waist-length hair. The terrible fever she endured during the journey caused all her hair to fall out. Upon her arrival in Sale Lake City she was wearing a wig Grandpa Sweyn had improvised from a horse's mane.

Grandpa Sweyn thought all the suffering and hardship were behind after his arrival in Salt Lake City, where he was given a responsible position as bookkeeper in the church storehouse. In the year 1874, he was called upon with others to volunteer for a mission to Utah's Dixie to help establish a colony to be named Enoch. He felt it his moral and religious duty to answer the call.

Before leaving Salt Lake City, Grandpa Sweyn took his two daughters to the Patriarch for his blessing. The Patriarch who had inherited his priesthood and calling was often asked to bless children within a prescribed jurisdiction. The blessings could be either oral or written.

The Patriarch placed his hand on the top of Sena, the elder of the two daughters. "This child shall be blessed with health, a long life and many children."

He then placed his hand on Tena's head. The old man seemed to rock back and forth. "This is an unusual child.

Her children shall bring beauty to the world, heal the sick, and spread the word of the Prophet."

In June of the year 1874 the Mission to Enoch left Salt Lake City. It consisted of one hundred twenty-four men, women and children. The wagon train followed the road along the foot of the Wasatch Range to Cedar City, then over the Plateau to Adenville, and from there northward ten miles to the place chosen by the scouts for the settlement.

The first winter presented many hardships, as excerpts from Grandpa Sweyn's diary show.

The terrible winter is passed, thank the Lord. While the climate was not too severe, there was a great deal of sickness and eight deaths. We have no doctors. Our medicine supplies of herbs, teas, catnip, peppermint, balsam, tansy, yarrow, slippery elm, spearmint, hops, horehound, sage, saffron and pine gum were woefully inadequate.

We discovered that sulphur and molasses could not only be used as a tonic but would cure many skin sores. The little olive oil we possessed was quickly used for earaches. The gum of pine trees we used to make poultices for drawing infected sores. A syrup made from onions and sugar proved to be the best remedy for colds. We treated bruises with a salve made of turpentine, mutton tallow and pine gum.

There would have been a good deal more sickness if we had not managed to keep clean. The good Lord wants his children to keep clean and He provided the way. We found the ashes of the cottonwood and willow trees rich in lye. The women put the ashes in a barrel and poured water on them. A leaching box fixed with a movable base which had ridged rows like a washboard was set in a slanting position to permit the lye to drain into a bucket. Grease added to the lye and boiled produces a soft soap that can be used for washing clothes. The friendly Indians showed us how to obtain a milder soap for washing the hair and the finest of materials. The root of the oose or yucca which grows wild in the hills makes a mild soap.

At the end of the first year, Grandpa Sweyn was more optimistic. He wrote in his diary:

We have very little fruit and milk except for the children's needs. But we now have an abundance of bread. We have no baking powder but plenty of leaven. The women obtain this from the alkali patches along the desert's edge, which they settle in water. The clear liquid is poured off and used for leaven to make bread.

The canal is completed. The ground fertile. We have planted many crops including peach pits we obtained from the Indians. We have to be constantly on the alert for the Paiutes. They are very friendly toward us, but seem unable to curb their tendency for taking anything they want.

I am leaving in a few days for Salt Lake City, where I will arrange to freight in the supplies I will need to stock my general store. My wife and I have had some lively discussions concerning the name. We have finally decided it will be called "Neilsen's Mercantile Store." It appears that I am assiduously obeying my brothers' command to be a shopkeeper.

In five years Enoch grew into a community of six hundred and forty people. Five hundred acres of farmland were under cultivation. The hard times were behind.

Grandpa did well with his store. He decided to build himself a new home and leave the log cabin in which he'd lived during those years. The new home had a bedroom downstairs and five bedrooms upstairs. Bishop Trainor called soon after the house was completed. He stood in the new home with his hands clasped behind his back and informed Grandpa it was an opportune time to take another wife. Like all Mormon communities of that time, Enoch had a surplus of single women due to the fact that the female converts always outnumbered the male.

"You can afford another wife and you have this big house," Bishop Trainor concluded.

"Brother Trainor," Grandpa Sweyn said soberly, "please do not approach me on the subject of polygamy again. It is an ordinance which I cannot subscribe to. I realize the need for plural marriages under the circumstances; but I find myself unable to even think about taking another wife for as long as my own lives."

Bishop Trainor respected the right of each individual to make the choice of embracing polygamy or refusing. He never mentioned the subject to Grandpa Sweyn again.

Nothing happened to upset the tranquillity of Grandpa Sweyn's life until Tom Fitzgerald came into it. At sixteen his daughter Sena had married a man named Bunderson, who did not believe in polygamy, and had moved to Emery, Utah Territory, soon after the marriage. He did not encourage his daughter Tena to marry so young. She was a great help to him in the store and he knew he and his wife would be lonely when she left home. He agreed with Bishop Trainor that Tena would marry Mark, the Bishop's son, when she was eighteen. It would be an ideal marriage. Neither he nor the Bishop had any doubts the two children would marry when they were of age. They had played together, been constant companions since they were children. Mark escorted Tena to all the church socials and dances. They went on hayrides and picnics together. They rode together. Grandpa Sweyn did not have the remotest idea his daughter didn't love Mark until she told him in her room that night when he asked her to tell the Gentile newspaper editor of her betrothal and impending marriage to the Bishop's son.

A few days after this event, Mark went for a ride with Tena on their saddle horses. At the edge of the desert, he drew his horse near to her. "There is something I must know, Tena. Are you going to marry me in the fall?"

She shook her head as tears came into her eyes. "Mark, I just can't. I love you, yes, but not that way. I love you as a brother. If I married you it wouldn't be fair to you. I would not feel that I was ever really yours. I can't explain it. I don't want to hurt you. I—I just don't love you that way."

He nodded slowly. "Then tell me, Tena, if you feel in your heart that in time you would learn to love me as a wife loves a husband?"

"I don't know, Mark. I honestly don't know."

"But your father and my father will insist that we marry when you are eighteen. Think, Tena. What if that day were tomorrow. What would you do?"

"Mark, you make me hurt you and I don't like to hurt you because I do love you, but not that way. I just couldn't marry you knowing that my feelings for you are not those of a girl in love."

"But your father will insist that you marry when you are eighteen. Tena, I would make you a good husband."

"I know, Mark. I wish I could say yes. But I love you too much as a friend, as a brother, to lie to you."

"Do you know what love is, Tena? Have you ever met a man who made you feel differently than I do?"

For a moment her face brightened. "Yes, Mark. For a brief moment with Tom Fitzgerald as I looked at him in our parlor I felt a strange new emotion I'd never felt in the presence of any man."

He nodded slowly. "You have answered my question, Tena. Now I know what I must do. Your happiness is the most important thing in my life."

8

THE COURTSHIP OF TENA

Tom Fitzgerald looked up from his desk in the office of *The Silverlode Advocate*. "Why, it's Mark Trainor, isn't it?" he said in surprise.

The Bishop's son shook hands and then sat down. "I want to talk to you, Tom Fitzgerald. Tell me first, why you insisted on hearing from Tena's own lips of her betrothal and coming marriage to me."

Tom cleared his throat and bared his soul. He told Mark of his mother and how she'd conditioned him into believing that somewhere in the world there was the one right girl for him. He told Mark of his college days and how he was always hoping the next girl he met would be the right one. His eyes brightened as he told of his first meeting with Tena. "She was the one," he said earnestly. "I knew the moment I first saw her. And I also tell you this, if there was any decent and honorable way for me to win Tena away from you, I would do so."

Mark Trainor nodded his head. "I am glad you said that. I have loved Tena since I was a boy. But she loves me only as a brother. She does not feel for me the love of a woman for a man she'll marry. I realize that if she did marry me, it would be only because her father and my father insisted upon it. I love her too much for that. I think only of her happiness. I saw something in her eyes as she looked at you in the parlor of her home that night which I would have given my life to see there as she looked at me. It struck me then that her happiness lies with you. My love for her is greater than my love for my father or my religion. I want Tena to be happy and I would do anything, anything to make her happy. Whether you are the man to make her happy, I don't know. She must have her chance for happiness, whether it be with you or some other man. I want you to see her again. There is a box supper dance and social at the Tabernacle in Enoch Saturday night. I'll point out the box prepared by Tena. You can then talk to her. Ask her to ride out with me and meet you near the wooded glen. The light in her eyes I saw that night may have been just the infatuation of a young girl for a handsome man. I must know. I want to give her every opportunity for happiness. Will you come?"

Tom's voice shook with emotion as he replied: "How can I thank you? I shall be everlastingly in your debt for your frankness and confidence. I swear to you that this love I feel for Tena is not a sudden thing. I have never given my body to another woman. I repeat that if I do not marry Tena, then I shall never marry."

Tom arrived in Enoch the following Saturday evening at twilight. He put up his horse and rig at the livery stable, washed up in the owner's home, and then walked to the Tabernacle. He was early and went into the chapel. The benches were hewn from white pine and matched the rostrum with its two rows of circular benches behind it. Steps on either side of the platform were hand carved. A Beethoven organ stood beneath the rostrum. Next to it was a plain table upon which were platters for the broken loaves of bread and trays of small glasses for water used in the Saints' Sacrament of Communion.

He sat there until he heard the sound of music coming from the social hall beneath the chapel, then descended the stairway at the side of the Tabernacle. As always, he was amazed at the talent for dancing displayed by the old and the young. The sound of laughter and voices became suddenly quiet. The musicians, consisting of a pianist, a violinist, a cello and a banjo player, stopped. Tom found himself the target of all eyes in the hall.

Bishop Trainor flanked by Sweyn Neilsen and another Mormon strode across the room. The Bishop stopped a few feet from Tom, clasped his hands behind his back. "You are not welcome here," he said in a voice made hoarse by excitement.

Tom looked him in the eye. "I have always attended the church socials in Adenville in my capacity as a journalist."

Bishop Trainor seemed at a loss for words for a moment. He finally spoke, "In that capacity only may you remain."

Tom sat down on the bench that lined the wall. Mormons near him began to edge away. The dancing began. He enjoyed watching the young children who danced with grace and agility. He had learned that all Mormons excelled in three things, riding, dancing and dexterity with firearms. He saw Mark Trainor dance by with Tena. As he watched her, he knew as surely as he knew his own name that she was the one girl for him.

The time came for the auction of the box supper. The

orchestra played a fanfare. The schoolteacher mounted the platform. Two men carried the big table piled high with the boxes which contained a card with the lady's name on it and a cold supper. They were mostly empty shoe boxes which had been trimmed in crepe paper and tied with ribbons. The schoolteacher picked up one and held it aloft.

"Brothers and Sisters, this box I hold before you is but one of the many awaiting the bids of the gentlemen present. There is no age limit. All males may bid. The money collected tonight is to buy more textbooks for our ever-growing school needs. Zion's children are increasing and we need more McGuffey Readers, more National Spellers and Geographies. The admission for tonight's dance was twenty-five cents. We could not accept spuds, pumpkins, eggs, chickens and so forth this time because we need cash to buy these books. We ask that you bid what you can afford. We hope to raise enough money tonight to purchase the McGuffey Readers. I will start the auction with this box. Who knows what fair and beautiful damsel prepared the supper in this box? Speak up, Brothers; the highest bidder not only gets his supper, but has the privilege of eating it with the beautiful lady who prepared it. Now, what am I bid?"

The highest bid of thirty-five cents was made by a boy of seventeen. Tom realized that the part to come was the biggest fun of the evening. All eyes watched the boy open the box and remove the name card in it. They saw his face turn red. They guffawed with laughter as the lad walked across the hall, bowed to a gray-haired grandmother and escorted her to the benches around the long table at the rear of the hall. The woman's husband called out to the boy, "Now don't be holding her hand under the table or trying to steal a kiss, Willie, because I'm watching you."

Tom was standing on the side of the hall with all the

other males present. The females all sat on the other side. As the auction proceeded, the male making the highest bid walked across the hall to claim his supper partner. Tom kept his eye on Mark Trainor. Finally Mark nodded his head as the schoolteacher held up a box tied with a blue ribbon.

"What am I bid, Brothers? What am I bid for this box filled with supper fit for a king and prepared by a queen. Who will be the lucky man to partake of this delicious supper and enjoy the company of a lovely damsel as well."

"One dollar," Tom said clearly.

A gasp came from the crowd. The highest bid of the evening had been sixty cents. The hall began to buzz with whispering. Sweyn Neilsen walked over to Bishop Trainor and said something to him. The Bishop nodded. He looked at his son.

Mark Trainor bid a dollar and a half to allay any suspicion of collusion.

Tom promptly bid two dollars.

Bishop Trainor entered the bidding. "Three dollars."

"Four dollars," Tom bid immediately.

Sweyn Neilsen whispered something in the Bishop's ear. Bishop Trainor nodded, then spoke loud enough for all to hear, "I wish to challenge the right of the gentleman to bid against me. He is here only as a journalist and not as a guest."

Tom looked at the schoolteacher. "Sir, my right to bid at the church box suppers in Adenville has never been questioned. My right to aid such a worthy cause as providing textbooks for school children surely can't be questioned. There are no public eating places in Enoch. I haven't had a bite to eat since noon. Surely, it is not in keeping with Latter-Day Saint hospitality to refuse a hungry man food."

Bishop Trainor watched the crowd with a trace of annoy-

ance on his face as he saw them nod their heads as if agree-
ing with Tom Fitzgerald. "I withdraw my objection," he
said. "Five dollars."

Tom Fitzgerald removed a leather pouch from his pocket.
He dumped several gold coins in his hand and began jin-
gling them. "Ten dollars," he said with determination.

"Ten dollars," the schoolteacher echoed with astonishment. It was the highest bid ever made at such a function.
"Ten dollars once. Ten dollars twice. Do I hear eleven
dollars? No. Ten dollars three times and sold to this gentleman."

Tom paid the money and claimed the box. He opened it
in a silence broken only by the hushed breathing of the
crowd. He looked at the card and smiled. He walked boldly
across the hall. He bowed in front of Tena Neilsen and
offered her his arm. She placed her hand on his arm and let
him escort her to the big table at the rear.

When they sat down, she blushed as she looked at him.
"I wish you hadn't come."

"I'm sorry if I've humiliated you," Tom said earnestly,
"but this is the only way I could see you and speak to you."

Bishop Trainor and Sweyn Neilsen sat down on either
side of them. Tom ignored them. "Even now with them
listening, I must speak to you. It grieves me to make a spectacle of you and myself but there is no alternative. I beg of
you permission to have you know me better. I know this is
very improper and rude, but I cannot help myself. I must
say what I feel. I love you, Tena Neilsen. I love you with the
intensity of the desert sun. I love you with the sweep and
grandeur of the mountain peaks. I love you with the humility of a peasant for a princess. I beseech you to grant me permission to see you again. Don't be afraid of the wrath of
your people. My love for you will shield and protect you."

Tena gripped her hands in her lap. She felt both frightened and thrilled. She rocked back and forth. This handsome man with his words of love created an emotional upheaval within her. She felt dizzy and unable to think coherently. Tears filled her eyes. "Please, please go away," she cried out piteously.

His face twisted in pain as if she'd wounded him. "I would die before I'd cause one tear to drop from your eyes," he said in a hushed voice. "I beg your forgiveness. My only defense for bringing this humiliation upon you is that I love you. I shall say it once again and then leave, I love you, Miss Tena." He stood up. "Remember, I shall ever be at your beck and call. Promise me that if you ever need me, you'll send for me."

Tena dropped her face into her hands. "I promise. I promise. Now, please go."

Tom reached down and grasped her hand. He pressed it to his lips amid the startled exclamations from the crowd. Sweyn Neilsen shouted, "See here, you young fool!"

Tom held his head and shoulders erect as he walked from the hall. But when he reached the street, he paused and leaned heavily against a tree. He felt a hand on his shoulder and turned to see Mark Trainor standing beside him.

"I'm sorry," the Bishop's son said sympathetically. "Maybe I was wrong."

Tom nodded. "It isn't so much for myself, but I'll never forgive myself for hurting her. The tears in her eyes were like daggers turning in my heart."

Tom couldn't remember the ride back to Silverlode. The empty ache in his heart seemed to spread slowly over his entire body, leaving him numb. Arriving in Silverlode, he put up the horse and buggy at the livery stable, and went to his room in the Miner's Hotel. He lay down fully clothed and stared at the ceiling. After a long time he got up and began pacing the floor. He could go to the Whitehorse Saloon and get drunk. That might dull the ache in his heart. But it would be back when the effects of the alcohol wore off. He would not desecrate his love for Tena by doing such a shameful thing. He could enter a monastery and in time find peace of mind and heart through prayer. But that would not be fair to God. To be a priest the desire to serve God must come from the very soul and not as an escape from reality. He dropped to his knees and clasping his hands, prayed for guidance.

When he awoke the next morning, he knew what he must do. Life to him was not a thing you choose as you do a suit of clothes, selecting the pattern, the color, the style. A man who could not face up to his own destiny was a coward. There was a newspaper to be edited and published. There was work to do. The ache in his heart was part of his destiny. He must learn to live with it.

Tena Neilsen did not sleep the night of the box supper, but lay awake in her bedroom until the sun began streaming through the window, going over and over her first meeting with Tom Fitzgerald. And each time, the part she remembered most was the impulse she'd had to reach across the counter and push back the cowlick of his curly black hair. She thought of their second meeting and again of the urge she'd felt to push back the cowlick of hair. She pictured the scene in the parlor of her home and of the almost uncontrollable desire she'd had to run across the room and touch his face with her hands. She closed her eyes and recalled what had happened at the box supper. She repeated the words of love he'd spoken to her and found herself pressing the hand he'd kissed against her own lips.

In the days that followed she prayed for strength to put him from her mind. But each time she saw a small boy she wondered what Tom had looked like when he was a boy. Every time she saw a couple walking arm in arm, she wondered how she would feel to be walking arm in arm with him. Then, one night she had a dream. She dreamed she was in his arms and he kissed her. She awoke trembling and her body wet from perspiration. She knew at last the meaning of love, and why she couldn't marry Mark. The next day she asked him to go riding with her.

At the edge of the desert, while they sat on a boulder, she poured out her heart to him. "I am being tortured," she concluded. "I cannot think of anything else. I can only think of him. He is nowhere near me and yet I feel his presence all the time. Help me, Mark. Please help me."

He took her hands in his. "It was I who rode to Silverlode and asked Tom Fitzgerald to come to the box supper, Tena."

She seemed startled.

He nodded. "I think only of your happiness, Tena. My love for you is such that I will sacrifice it to make you happy. I have felt since that night in your parlor that you and Tom Fitzgerald belong to each other. I know he is a Gentile and you a Mormon; but you must not be afraid. I know how deeply and sincerely he loves you. You must find out, Tena, whether you love him enough to marry him. Let me bring him to you."

She threw back her head and her face became radiant. "I

will, Mark. I will. I'll write him a letter and you can deliver
it for me."

Two days later Mark Trainor entered the office of *The
Silverlode Advocate,* where he found the editor seated at a
roll-top desk. He shook hands and removed the letter from
the pocket of his buckskin vest.

The letter read in part:

I write this epistle with my heart and my heart tells me I
must see you as quickly as possible. I must talk to you. Please
come. I need you.

A few days later, Tena went riding with Mark. They met
Tom near a wooded glen a few miles from Enoch on the
road to Silverlode. While Mark watched the horses, Tena
and Tom walked and talked.

Many years later when we children asked Mamma what
she and Papa said to each other during that meeting, a soft
light would come into her brown eyes. She'd stop whatever
she was doing and go into a sort of a trance. Then she'd
shake her head and say: "There are some moments in every
woman's life which are too precious to share with anyone,
even her own children."

They met several times afterward at the wooded glen, but
the crisis in their love was developed through correspond-
ence, with Mark Trainor acting as their trusted messenger.
Tom wrote in one letter of the difference in their religious
faiths,

My beloved Tena,
I am not a wise man. But this I know, that God in His infinite
wisdom did not mean love should be denied any of his children

because they seek to worship Him in different churches. I believe that God is to religion as the ocean is to the many rivers that wind their way until they empty themselves into it. It is the belief in God that really matters, and the manner in which we manifest that belief is but a tributary to it. I could not possibly love you more if you were a Catholic.

And now, my beloved, please promise not to read the final paragraph until you are alone in your room and the moon is shining.

You have waited, my dearest Tena, as I knew you would. Walk to your window. Look up at the western sky. Ask yourself: How many ways does Tom love me? You will find the answer in the sky. You can count the many ways I love you, my dear, only by counting all the stars you see.

Good night, my dear, a sweet good night.

Tena knew she loved Tom. She could not understand why she didn't heed his plea and Mark's suggestion that they elope. It wasn't so much the thought of hurting her father and mother, for she had a premonition that in time they would both forgive her. She disliked deceiving them into believing that the rides she and Mark took were for the purpose of young lovers being alone. It was the grip the Latter-Day Saint religion had upon her conscience that held her back.

She received a letter from Tom telling her of his father's sudden death from pneumonia. He promised to return from Pennsylvania before her eighteenth birthday.

Tom's grief over the death of his father was mitigated by the joy in seeing his brother, Father John, and his sisters Josie and Cathie again. He did not mention that he was in love with a Mormon girl. When they pleaded with him to remain in Boylestown and take over the newspaper and other estate matters, he reminded them of his promise to his mother.

The estate was amicably settled. He received several thousand dollars in bonds and securities in lieu of the property which was part of his inheritance, and turned the property over to his sisters. Grandpa Timothy had cut his son Will off without a penny, inserting in his will as a reason: "The devil looks out for his own children."

When Tom alighted from the stagecoach in Silverlode, he found Mark Trainor leaning against one of the posts that supported the balcony over the stage depot. Mark was whittling, and from the pile of shavings on the sidewalk he must have been waiting a long time. He shut his pocketknife and dropped it into his pocket. He met Tom with a warm handclasp. "I don't know what I would have done if you hadn't been on this stagecoach," he said. "I've been meeting every one for the past week."

Tom became alarmed. "Has anything happened to Tena?"

Mark shook his head. "Nothing except that she'll be eighteen in a week and her father and my father are going right ahead with the wedding plans. I have a letter for you from Tena." He didn't hand Tom the letter until they were in the hotel room. "I think you'll want to read this over in private. I'll wait downstairs."

With trembling hands, Tom opened the letter.

My dearest,
If this crass betrayal of my heart for not telling you how much I love you before you went away means a lifelong regret,

I deserve it for my cowardice. I pray that I am not too late in saying, yes, yes, I love you, my dearest. Yes, yes, I'll marry you, dear Tom.

I love you truly. I love you deeply. I love you now. I'll love you forever. I love you more than my father, my mother, my religion. I love you as Ruth loved in the Bible. I have carefully weighed the consequences of my love for you and they are as nothing compared to the consequences I would suffer were I to go on denying that love. Thy God shall be my God. Thy people shall be my people. Come for me, my dear, dear Tom, and take me for your wife. If prayers will bring you, I know you will come.

> I subscribe myself with love,
> *Tena*

Tears were streaming down Tom's cheeks when he finished reading. He folded the letter and tenderly placed it in his pocket. From an elkhorn hatrack he removed his holster and gun, and joined Mark in the hotel lobby. He forgot how tired he was from the long journey and insisted they leave for Enoch at once. They rented two fast saddle horses from Tanner's Livery Stable. Mark had his own horse. After dark they arrived at the farmhouse of an apostate Mormon on the outskirts of Enoch, where they slept in blankets on the floor. The next morning the apostate's wife cooked them a breakfast of flapjacks, steak, eggs, sour-dough biscuits and honey.

They thanked their host, who refused any payment, and rode to the wooded glen where they'd met so many times. Mark turned sideways in his saddle. "Tom, I'm going to try and talk you out of doing it this way just once more. Today is Sunday. You'll arrive in town just as everybody is on his way to church. Why not wait until tomorrow? I'll have Tena ride with me and meet you here."

Tom shook his head. "Forgive me, Mark, for being so obstinate about this but I cannot help myself. I am not going to take Tena from her father like a thief in the night. I want her father and mother to know that we are eloping."

Mark shrugged, and a grin wrinkled his freckled nose. "They'll know all right if you insist on doing it this way. The whole town will know. It is just that until Tena is eighteen she is a minor and they might make trouble for you. Well, good luck. I'll be waiting right here."

Tena was walking toward the Tabernacle with her family when she heard the sound of galloping hoofs. She recognized Tom even from a distance. She was smiling when he stopped the horse beside her and, leaning over, held out his hand. With a glad cry she placed her hand in his and felt herself pulled by his strong arm to the back of the horse. She wrapped her arms around Tom's chest and and nestled her head against his back as he wheeled the horse and sent it at a gallop toward Silverlode. She heard her father cry out, "Come back, daughter, come back!"

They met Mark at the wooded glen, where he helped Tena mount the spare horse they'd brought from Silverlode. When Tom asked if she could stand the ride, Mark laughed: "She can outride any man. Just try to keep up with her. I've cut the telegraph lines to Adenville. When they find they can't get a message through, they'll probably send a posse up Indian Canyon and down the other side of the range. They know you can't be married in Silverlode. They'll figure you'll have to go to Salt Lake to get a licence and be married there. They will try to head you off at Cedar City or above there. Now, Tom, before you go—" Mark pulled his horse closer and looked steadily into Tom's eyes. "You know, of course, that I'll kill you if you ever hurt Tena or bring her any unhappiness?"

Tom held out his hand. "I'd want it that way, Mark.

Some day in some way I hope I can repay you for all you've done for Tena and me."

"You repay me by making Tena happy," Mark smiled. "Goodbye and good luck to you both."

When they arrived in Silverlode, Tom was afraid to leave Tena in *The Advocate* office or a hotel for fear the Mormons would find her. In desperation he took her up the back way to Uncle Will's suite of rooms above the White-horse Saloon. That would probably be the last place in Silverlode the Mormons would think of looking. Queenie was on a shopping trip to Salt Lake City. A Chinese servant went to fetch Uncle Will.

When Uncle Will met Tena he bowed as he took her hand and kissed it with old-world courtesy. "Beautiful Princess," he said, "I never believed a flower so fair could bloom in this rough country. I have heard some talk that my brother was secretly paying court to a woman; but never believed it could be one as beautiful and charming as you. Consider me, Will Fitzgerald, your servant. You have but to make a wish, Princess, and the wish shall be my command."

Tena blushed as she withdrew her hand. She had never met a man like Uncle Will. "You are very gallant," she smiled.

Tom quickly explained the elopement to his brother.

Uncle Will waved his arm. "Let there be music. Let there be a bountiful feast. Let there be dancing in the streets. Let the misbegotten sons of peasants who inhabit this dreary place pay homage to a Princess."

"Please stop the flowery speeches," Tom said, "this is serious. Our immediate concern is not to be seen in Silverlode and to get past the Mormon patrols between here and Salt Lake City. Tena will not be of age for another week."

"No sooner said than done," Uncle Will smiled. "I shall provide you with an armed escort of assorted gunmen, including myself, who can shoot their way through a troop of cavalry."

Tom shook his head violently. "I won't stand for any shooting, Will."

Uncle Will hooked his thumb in the belt of his jeweled holster. "You can't expect the Princess to make the long journey around the mountain range and across the desert by horseback, Tom. That is all Indian and outlaw country. We'll discuss it further over something to eat." He called the Chinese servant and ordered luncheon.

Tena was fascinated by the gold-rimmed china service, the gold-plated knives, forks and spoons, the exquisite cut-glass water tumblers, the imported tablecloth and the luxurious furnishings. She had never seen such elegance. She complimented the Chinese servant upon the wild duck cooked with rice which was the main course of the luncheon.

They discussed and discarded many plans for outwitting the Mormon patrols. It was Tena herself who provided the idea for the plan they adopted.

"I remember when I was a little girl and we were crossing the plains. Our wagon train was attacked at one place by Indians. My father hid my sister and me in one of the big empty water bottles on the side of our wagon."

Uncle Will rubbed his waxed mustache. "It might work at that. There are three big freighters pulling out of here empty this afternoon. I don't believe a posse would think of looking for you in a freighter. But if they do, those water barrels they have on them are big enough for a person to hide in. You could hide in the water barrels going through Cedar City. It's worth a try. And, Tom, don't worry. If anything happens, I'll take enough of the boys to head that posse off coming back down Indian Canyon and rescue the Princess from them."

Grandpa Sweyn was loath to join the posse that Bishop Trainor organized as soon as he discovered the telegraph wires to Adenville had been cut. The long hard ride over the mountain range was a grueling ordeal for a man unaccustomed to the saddle. He was stiff and sore when they arrived at their destination, a place in the road several miles above Cedar City. County Sheriff Hank Jeffers had ridden over from Adenville to join them.

Bishop Trainor sent six members of the posse into Cedar City with instructions to stop all travelers going northward and search for Tena. He took command of the other seven members of the posse. The place he'd chosen gave an uninterrupted view of the desert for miles. The road at this point ran right under the overhanging perpendicular sandstone cliffs. It would be impossible for any traveler going to Salt Lake City from Cedar City to pass without being seen.

It was almost dusk when three empty freight wagons were sighted coming from the direction of Cedar City. The wagons had made two stops not in their original schedule. They had stopped just before reaching Cottonwood Canyon Station while two passengers climbed into the big water barrels on the side of the middle wagon. For the same reason they stopped once more before entering Cedar City. Just before rounding the ridge from the mountain range that shut off the view to the north, the freighters again stopped. The lead driver spoke to his passengers. "Better hop back in those barrels. If there's any place between here and Salt Lake for a posse to be waiting it'll be about two miles north of here."

When the lead driver found eight armed men blocking the road, he pulled his six span of mules to a halt.

Bishop Trainor spoke. "We mean you no harm. We just want to search your wagons for a runaway girl who is a minor. We have a duly executed warrant for her arrest."

The driver spat some tobacco juice over the side. "Search and be damned. Armed men've searched these wagons already half a dozen times. One more time won't hurt none."

Grandpa Neilsen kneed his horse to the side of the middle wagon where he remained until Bishop Trainor signaled the driver the search was over and the freighters could move on. Grandpa didn't tell anybody for years that the reason he guided his horse to the side of the freighter was that he saw a piece of blue cloth through the bunghole in the water barrel, and recognized it as being the same color as the dress his daughter was wearing that morning.

He was, perhaps, thinking back to his own marriage to Elizabeth Fairgate and how his own people and her people had disowned them because of religion. Perhaps he was thinking of how happy he and Elizabeth had been, and the depth of their devotion to each other. He could have taken his daughter away from Tom Fitzgerald, but instead he helped them elope.

9

HONEYMOON AND HOME

P<small>APA AND MAMMA</small> were married in Salt Lake City by a Gentile District Judge, with a newspaper editor and a lawyer as witnesses. Mamma lied about her age. This was the first of four times that Papa and Mamma were married to each other.

Papa helped Mamma select a trousseau and they left for Denver over the newly completed Denver and Rio Grande Railway.

Mamma never told us children much about her honeymoon until after Papa died. Then, when we'd see her rocking back and forth, her eyes closed and a smile on her lips, we'd ask, "Are you lonesome for Papa?" She'd shake her head. "I shall never be lonesome because I can borrow Papa from my memories any time I need him. Did I ever tell you children about the time Papa and I—" and Mamma would then share some personal part of their lives with us children.

Papa had tickets for a lower and an upper berth in the Pullman car. While he smoked a cigar in the smoker, Mamma undressed and went to bed in the lower berth. Papa returned. He bent over and kissed the long braids of her hair which lay on top of the blanket. He looked into her eyes and kissed her gently on the lips. "I ask only this, my dearest Tena girl, that not until your desire for me is as great as my own for you, will I share a bed with you."

Mamma admitted she was grateful because she was a little frightened. She and Papa had actually been in each other's company very little. "Thank you, dear Tom," she said, and while he held her hand she fell asleep. Then Papa climbed into the upper berth.

Papa had telegraphed for a sitting room and two bedrooms at the Windsor Hotel in Denver. They spent the first few days of their honeymoon sight-seeing and getting married again upon Mamma's eighteenth birthday. They were wed in a civil ceremony.

The night of their second marriage, Papa took Mamma to Charpiot's Restaurant at 386 Larimer Street for dinner. Mamma was overwhelmed by the elegance of the "Delmonico of the West." They went to the Tabor Grand Opera House after dinner to see the Maggie Mitchell Company in *Mignon*. After the opera they stopped at the Vienna Cafe, at 372 Curtis Street, for an after-theater supper. It was quite late when they entered their sitting room in the Windsor Hotel.

Papa took Mamma in his arms for what he thought was to be his usual good-night kiss. Mamma's lips clung hungrily to his and she whispered passionately, "Tom, my dearest, Tom."

The next morning, Papa informed the hotel clerk that a single bedroom would suffice. They began shopping for their furniture the next day. Before leaving Silverlode Papa had arranged with Uncle Will to buy the Ferguson property in Silverlode, next to the Aden Irrigation Ditch. Uncle Will had insisted that the property and the house he would build upon it be his wedding present. "That will give you enough money and time for a real honeymoon," he said.

When Papa had tried to tell Uncle Will what kind of house he wanted built, Uncle Will replied, "Don't tell me, Tom. I know what kind of house to build for a Princess."

Mamma saved all the programs from the Tabor Opera House and the menus from Charpiot's, Elitch's, the Oyster House and the Vienna Cafe, all of which Papa had tipped the headwaiters to autograph. After Papa died I remember many times seeing Mamma go up to our attic. She'd open a trunk and remove the programs of *La Traviata, Martha, Heart and Hand, The Bohemian Girl* or *Il Trovatore,* all of which she'd seen and heard with Papa, performed by the Abbott Company with Emma Abbott. She'd tell in great detail the story of the operas and describe the beautiful costumes. Then in fancy she'd take us children to one of the famous restaurants and we'd pretend to order from the menus. And Mamma would describe the famous dishes she and Papa had eaten. I also remember how Mamma would often caress a piece of furniture and tell us about the shop in Denver where it had been purchased.

Papa and Mamma returned to Silverlode two months after their elopement. The stagecoach was late in arriving because the lead horse had thrown a shoe, and it was after dark when it pulled to a stop in front of the stage depot.

Whiskey Row was deserted. A cold wind was blowing hard and the ground was frozen under the snow. Papa took only two pieces of luggage, leaving the rest at the depot, and he and Mamma walked with their heads down for protection against the icy wind until they'd crossed Corry Street. Then Papa pointed, "Look, dear. No wonder Will didn't meet us. He must be having a welcome home party."

The house he pointed to at the end of Whiskey Row was

an extravagant imitation of some Second Empire mansion, complete with towers and porches. Lights gleamed from the big bay windows. Papa felt Mamma's hand trembling on his arm.

"It—it seems like such a big house," she said.

"That's my brother for you," Papa said with pride.

They heard the sound of music and loud laughter as they approached the house. Papa raised the heavy brass knocker on the oak door. People or no people, he promised himself he would carry his bride across the threshold.

The big door swung open, and Papa frowned. Dandy Allen waved the bottle of whiskey he was holding and shouted, "Welcome to the housewarming, Tom!"

Papa stared past Allen into the parlor of the house, which was bare of furniture except for the piano he'd secretly bought as an extra surprise for Mamma. Some wooden planks had been placed on beer kegs to make a bar. An orchestra composed of a pianist, a fiddler and a banjo player was making a fearful din. The place was filled with dance hall girls, miners, drifters and gamblers.

Dandy Allen smiled. "Hope you don't mind us using your piano, Tom. There wasn't any place to store it."

Papa took a deep breath. "But I do mind. And I especially mind your unmitigated nerve in assembling all the riff-raff in Silverlode in my home. Get them out, Dandy. Get them out at once, or I'll personally throw every last one of them out."

"Hold your horses, Tom." Dandy said in as level a voice as he could manage. "This happens to be my house, not yours. These are my guests and not yours. I won this house from Will in a poker game last night."

Knowing his brother as he did, Papa didn't doubt the story for a moment. He picked up the valise and satchel.

"Come, Tena girl," he said fighting to hold back his anger at his brother.

Mamma did not speak until they had almost reached the Miner's Hotel. She placed her hand on his arm. "I know you are angry at your brother, Tom dear. But I am glad. I didn't like the house. It's just too big and gaudy. It was nothing like the home I dreamed about."

Papa shrugged. "My own brother! To think my own brother could do this to me. I should have known better than to trust him." He stopped as they reached the door of the Miner's Hotel and looked at her tenderly. "Perhaps it is for the best, Tena girl. To tell the truth, I didn't care much for the house either. We'll have to spend the night in the hotel. Tomorrow we will go to Salt Lake and stay there until I build you the kind of house we both want."

Mamma shook her head. "Silverlode is our home and we'll stay right here in this hotel until our new house is built. I know you are very anxious about *The Advocate*."

"Thank you, my dear. But the Miner's Hotel isn't a proper place for a respectable woman. We'll talk it over in the morning."

Charlie Gruber, the hotel clerk, handed Papa a key after he'd signed the register. "It's the key for the Clayton boys' room, Tom. It's a much larger and better room than yours. I asked the boys to move into yours when I heard about Will losing the house. I'm sorry, Tom, for you and the Missus."

Mamma smiled at him. "You are very kind and thoughtful."

Papa opened the door of Room 116. He picked Mamma up in his arms and carried her into the room with its peeling, faded wallpaper. Before putting her down he kissed her.

Placing his hands on her shoulders, he looked at her. "Are you sorry you married me, Tena girl?"

She stood on her tiptoes and kissed him. "Don't ever ask such a foolish question again, my darling."

The next morning they went to the Erin Cafe for breakfast. Bridget O'Flynn put her big hands on her wide hips and said, "Sure, 'tis a broth of a lass ye have for a bride, Tom." She smiled at Mamma, " 'Tis a real beauty ye are."

The food was plain but good. Papa was pleased to see Mamma eating with appetite and taking everything in her stride. They had just finished when Mark Trainor entered the Cafe. He came over to the table, offered his congratulations, and accepted Papa's invitation to sit down. He hung his hat on a peg and ran his hand through his straw-colored hair.

"I was in the Whitehorse Saloon the other night," he said, "when your brother lost the house, Tom. They were playing for high stakes. Allen was having a streak of luck. I've heard how your brother goads Allen into playing when Dandy is a heavy loser. The other night the tables were turned. Allen kept winning. Then, he pushed all his chips into the center of the table and offered to bet them against the house. Your brother offered to bet money or the Whitehorse Saloon itself, but not the house. Allen reminded him of all the times the gambler had accumulated enough of a stake to go into business for himself, only to have your brother win it from him. He said he wanted the house so he could open a gambling hall in it. Your brother looked at Allen. He said that if he wouldn't miss having the gambler around, he'd just go ahead and kill him. Instead, he called Allen's play.

A hand of show down poker was dealt, and Allen won the house. Your brother offered to bet the Whitehorse Saloon, which is worth twenty times what the house is, on another hand, but Allen refused to play any more."

Papa shook his head slowly. "I don't blame my brother. I blame myself. I know my brother better than any man does. There is only one thing to do. Tena and I'll go to Salt Lake and remain there until I can have a house built."

Mark scratched his jaw with his finger. "I was coming to that. I own a house in Adenville just the other side of the ditch. It's a small adobe place with a sitting room, a big kitchen and one bedroom. Tena could make a home of it."

Mamma leaned forward and looked searchingly at Mark. "Aren't you living in Enoch any more, Mark?"

He smiled and shrugged his shoulders. "When I took sides against my father and my religion to help you two elope, I felt I couldn't live at home any longer. I bought that saddlery shop next to *The Advocate,* and enlarged it to include a harness and gun shop. I'm good at that sort of thing. I always liked working with leather and I know guns. No reason I can't become a fair gunsmith."

Papa patted Mark on the shoulder. "I am sorry if I have been the reason for your leaving home."

"It wasn't because of you, Tom. It's something I've been wanting to do for some time. But let's go back to the adobe house. It won't hold all the furniture you shipped here and that's stored in Tanner's Livery Stable. But I can store what you can't use in the rear of my shop."

Papa shook his head. "I don't know what to say, Mark. I had such big plans for our home."

Mamma put her hand into Papa's. "Please Tom, let's go see Mark's house."

The house and the picket fence had been recently whitewashed. Mamma looked at it from the street. "It's lovely," she exclaimed. "Lots of space for a nice lawn in front and room enough in the backyard for a vegetable garden."

Mark held open the gate and they walked up the cinder path. As they entered the house, Papa was astonished at the size of the combination parlor, living room and dining room, which ran the full width of the house. The kitchen was very large, with a pantry between it and the bedroom.

Mamma rushed eagerly from room to room. "It is just what I wanted," she cried happily. "Come now, Tom, don't look so mortified. I feel right at home in this house and I would never have felt that way in that monstrosity your brother built. Now off you go. Promise not to return until supper time. Hire two strong men and have them bring all the furniture, including the piano that Allen person has. I'll have the men take back what I don't use and store it in the rear of Mark's shop."

"But Tena girl," Papa protested, "there is so much to do. Perhaps Mark and I could help."

Mamma shook her head. "Please, Tom dear, let me do it. This is my first home and a woman loves to fix up her house herself." She stood on her tiptoes and kissed him, then turned to Mark. "I could not love you more if you were my real brother," she said, and planted a kiss on his cheek that made him blush.

When Papa and Mark reached the street, Papa held out his hand. "It seems that I'm destined to go through life being in your everlasting debt, Mark. No man ever had a better friend. I know you haven't been living in that house."

Mark fell in step as they walked toward Silverlode. "I should have at least put an old iron bed in the place," he smiled. "When your brother lost the house to Allen, I knew I had only one day to find you a new home. Your brother had told everyone when he expected you to return. The adobe house was owned by a Mormon family that outgrew it. They moved out of it a few weeks ago. I rode down to the farm they bought and where they are now living, and bought the house from them."

Papa nodded. "I want to ask you one more favor, Mark. Will you sell me the house?"

"I was hoping you'd say that, Tom. I had to borrow money on my shop to buy it."

They went to the Silverlode Bank where Papa paid Mark for the house. As was customary, the signing of papers would come later. They said goodbye outside the bank.

Papa walked across the street to where the Parker brothers were sitting in front of the Emporium, husky Mormon boys who hired out to Gentiles to do work as handy men. Papa asked them if they'd help move the furniture. They shook their heads. Suddenly Papa realized that this was the beginning of the Mormons' ostracism of himself and Tena.

He crossed Corry Street and saw Windy Davis coming out of the Whitehorse Saloon. "Windy," Papa said, "get two Chinamen to help you and go to the adobe house just the other side of Aden Ditch. Mrs. Fitzgerald is there. She will tell you what to do. There will be five dollars in it for you and five dollars for each of the Chinese."

Windy squinted at Papa as he said dubiously, "There ain't no chance your wife'll want me to dig in, is there Tom? You know me and work's been strangers for years."

"No, Windy. You tell her you are there to see the Chinamen work. And stay sober, Windy. I'll go over to the livery stable and arrange for a team and wagon for you to haul the furniture, while you round up a couple of Chinamen. When you finish, come to *The Advocate* office and I'll pay you."

Papa went into the Whitehorse Saloon before going to the livery stable, and went upstairs to his brother's suite of rooms. When he knocked, Queenie called for him to come in. She and his brother were having a late breakfast.

Dressed in a quilted dressing gown, Uncle Will leaned back in his chair. "Get it off your chest, Tom, so I can continue my breakfast."

Papa shrugged, "There are a lot of things I could say."

Uncle Will placed an elbow on the table and pointed a long tapering finger at Papa. "If you're waiting for me to say I'm sorry, Tom, you'll have a long wait. I've never apologized to a man in my life and I'm not going to start now. I will say only this. I had to call Dandy's hand or leave Silverlode. The only other alternative would have been to kill him. And I didn't think the damn house was worth killing a man, especially one I like."

"Forget the house, Will. Allen did me and Tena a favor when he won it from you. It wasn't the kind of house either of us wanted. The reason I came to see you was that I just wanted to make sure you weren't planning any kind of revenge on Allen on my account. I'll see you later. Goodbye, Queenie."

Dave Powell was seated in the swivel chair at the roll-top desk in *The Advocate* office, his green eyeshade pushed back to the middle of his head. His hips lapped over the arms of the chair like folded blankets. He got to his feet when he saw Papa. "Tom," he cried, "welcome back."

They discussed Papa's trip and then the local news. Papa was relieved to learn the Mormons hadn't cancelled their subscriptions and were still bringing in their advertising and printing.

Dave pulled up a chair while Papa sat in the swivel chair. "Bishop Aden," Powell said, "came to see me the day after you left. He said he wanted to impress on me that the Mormons would seek no retaliation and hoped the editorial policy of *The Advocate* would remain unbiased. And here's one that's hard to believe. He gave me a check for over three hundred subscriptions for Mormons in Enoch and other communities. Said to just send *The Advocate* by stagecoach to Enoch in care of Neilsen's Mercantile Store. Knowing Neilsen was your father-in-law, I couldn't help but ask the Bishop what was behind it all. He gave me a damn good answer. Said that it would be newspapers like *The Advocate* which would one day make Utah a state."

Papa had a hard time concentrating on his work that day. He worried about Windy not staying sober. He worried about the weather—the sky was gray and it looked as if it might snow. He worried about Mamma working too hard. He went to the Whitehorse with Powell for a glass of beer and a couple of sandwiches for lunch. The afternoon seemed to drag by. It was almost five o'clock before Windy entered the office with two Chinamen.

Windy rubbed the sleeve of his leather jacket across his forehead. "Never seed such a woman for gittin' things done. Tell you somethin', Tom. Missus Fitzgerald's the first person, man or woman, ever got any work out of Windy Davis since I can't remember when. My back's breakin' and my muscle's achin'. But the whole shootin' match is done."

Papa gave the men a five-dollar gold piece each, and removed his apron and eyeshade. A flurry of snowflakes fell as he opened the gate of the picket fence. Mamma, dressed in high-necked shirtwaist, bustle skirt and high-buttoned shoes, ran down the cinder path to meet him. She twined her arm in his. "It's our first home, Tom, and I love it."

"I bought it from Mark," he said.

"I knew you would," she smiled. "Now, carry your bride across the threshold. It will be a fitting sight for that nosy neighbor across the street who's been peeking through her curtains all day."

Papa carried her into their first home. He kissed her and reluctantly put her down. His eyes traveled around the large room. "Why—it's unbelievable," he cried.

The green Brussels carpet with a flowered design Mamma had picked out in Denver wasn't long enough to cover the entire wooden floor, but the oval braided rag rug in front of the blazing fireplace made up for the shortage. Brass tongs and a box of cordwood stood on one side of the fireplace; the bookcase and books they'd bought in Denver on the other side. The big glass mirror with its gilt-edge frame hung above the mantel. Two blue vases with fluted tops, and statues of a shepherd and a shepherdess that Mamma had found in a Denver antique shop, decorated the mantelpiece. The comfortable mohair spring rocking chair Papa had chosen was in front of the fireplace, with Mamma's maple rocking chair beside it. The piano stood in one corner; the leather-covered sofa against one wall and the two matching chairs against the other. Above the sofa hung an oblong clock and two colored prints. In the center of the room was a marble-top oval shaped table.

Mamma held out her hand and led Papa to inspect the bedroom, and then the kitchen. Papa was amazed that Mamma had found time to scrub the white pine floor. The Jewel cook stove already had a fire going in it. The kitchen was so large that the drop-leaf extension oak table and six matching chairs placed at one end of it still left room for several unopened crates which were piled up near it.

A small washstand with tin basin and soap dish stood near the rear door. Mamma placed her hands on her hips. "Being so near Aden Ditch, we won't have to carry water far. Some day, we'll put down a well and have a pump right in our kitchen."

Papa shook his head. "I don't believe there are any wells in Adenville, my dear."

"There is water all right," Mamma said. "With all the sandstone formations in the canyon, that water has to drain off toward the mouth of the canyon. You wait and see. Some day we'll have a pump right in our kitchen. And now, my dear husband, I shall prepare you our first meal in our home. It won't be anything special because there really wasn't too much time."

She insisted he sit in his rocking chair and have a cigar. She turned up the kerosene lamp that hung suspended from a rafter above and handed him a book. When he offered to help, she shook her head. "This is woman's work. Don't expect a banquet. Mister Davis was unable to get me all the things I needed at the Emporium."

Papa laughed. "That is probably the first time anybody ever called Windy, Mister."

Mamma cocked her head to one side. "I thought him a very fine fellow. A bit dirty and uncouth, perhaps. But a gentleman in many ways. He was really very helpful."

"You mean that Windy actually did some of the work?"

This question seemed to surprise Mamma. "He did most of it. I couldn't trust those Chinamen with some of the things. I was afraid they wouldn't understand and might break or scratch the furniture."

Papa shook his head. "I can't believe it. Windy Davis of all people!"

Mamma still seemed puzzled. "There is good in all people, if you but look for it. You must have seen some good in Mister Davis or you wouldn't have sent him to help me."

"I'm sorry, Tena girl, but I didn't mean it that way. What I meant was that Windy hasn't done a lick of work since coming to Silverlode."

"Perhaps," Mamma said walking toward the kitchen, "it's because nobody ever offered the man a job. And when we get settled, Tom, I want you to bring him for supper some night. I promised him a good home-cooked meal."

Papa merely shook his head with bewilderment.

Their first meal tasted better to Papa than any of the fancy meals they'd eaten in Denver. It was the first time he'd ever tasted Mormon gravy. Mamma had made it by adding flour to the grease left from frying the home-cured ham, allowed it to brown, then added milk, and salt and pepper. She poured it over hot biscuits. Mamma had made coffee for Papa, but being a Mormon, she herself drank milk. When she served the apple pie, she smiled, "No, Tom dear, I didn't have time to make a pie. I told Mister Davis I didn't have anything for dessert, so he got the pie for me from a Mrs. Burke who runs a boarding house."

The first night in their home, Papa stood behind Mamma in the bedroom while she brushed her long blonde hair in the light of the kerosene lamp. He looked tenderly at her reflection in the mirror above the dresser. "Tena girl, I shall love you and cherish you for always, and always."

She smiled. "Please do, Tom dear."

He put his hands gently on her shoulders. "It's going to be difficult for you because, I'm afraid, the Mormons of Adenville will ostracize us."

She moved her head and kissed his hand. "The one and only thing in the world of which I am afraid, Tom dear, is that some day you will no longer love me."

Papa moved to the side of the chair. He dropped to his knees. "That day, my darling, will never be."

10

PAPA DECIDES TO BECOME A MORMON

PAPA KNEW that Mamma's life was very lonely. The Latter-Day Saints politely ignored her because she was an apostate. They would not let her trade in Adenville; even the farmers refused to sell her eggs and vegetables. She had to depend upon Abe Glassman's Emporium for all her needs. Unbeknown to Mamma, he carefully wrote down everything she asked for which he didn't have and either bought the items from the Mormons or sent to Salt Lake City for them. For a long, long time, Mamma never knew that the bolts of cloth, thread, needles, and dozens of other items Abe carried in stock, had but a single customer.

Papa worried a great deal more than Mamma. She would walk down Whiskey Row, stopping to speak to Windy Davis whether he was drunk or sober, and as she got to know people, she often might be seen talking to Butch Mears, Chinamen, Judge Baker, gamblers and miners. Papa wanted to protest when he first saw Mamma smile and say good morning to some dance hall girls. He put his foot down one time when Uncle Will happened to mention that one of the dance hall girls was very ill, but it didn't stop Mamma from going up the rear entrance to the Whitehorse Saloon, and helping

Queenie nurse the girl back to health. Papa never got over the way Mamma seemed to bring out the hidden good in everybody she met. Men who had never tipped their hats to a lady in their lives always did when they passed Mamma. Every Saturday Windy Davis remained cold sober. He presented himself at the adobe house, cleaned the yard, weeded the garden, cut wood and did other chores for Mamma. He refused to accept any pay for his work except a home-cooked meal. At first Gabby Harnett, the barber, thought Windy had gone plumb crazy when he showed up early one Saturday morning, took a bath, and then got a shave.

The thought that there weren't any decent married women in Silverlode for Mamma to associate with worried Papa to the point where he offered himself as a convert to Mormonism one evening when he met Bishop Aden. "Mind if I walk a ways with you, Bishop Aden?" he asked.

Bishop Aden's blue eyes looked out from beneath the wide-brimmed black hat he wore, with an expression of mild surprise. "Not at all," he answered.

Papa fell in step as they walked down Adenville's main street. "Do you hate me because I married a Mormon?" he asked.

Bishop Aden pulled at the stub of his partially shot-off ear. "We Saints hate no man. We strive to love our neighbors."

"But," Papa protested, "I've noticed a strained relationship between us since my marriage. Believe me, sir, I love my wife as no other man could possibly love a woman. I worship and adore her."

"We Saints," the Bishop rebuked him gently, "love our women but worship and adore only the Lord."

"I'm sorry," Papa apologized, "it was just a figure of speech. The point I'm trying to make is that I love my wife more than I do my own Catholic religion. I've been seriously considering joining the Latter-Day Saints Church. I know it would make my wife happy and remove all ostracism."

Bishop Aden frowned. "To embrace a religious faith because of earthly love for a woman is unworthy of the high esteem in which I hold you, Tom Fitzgerald."

"The high esteem?" Papa echoed.

"Why should that surprise you?" Bishop Aden said. "You have many qualities of character which I admire and that is why what you just said disappoints me. A religious faith can only be based upon a spiritual awakening. You desecrate not only my faith but your own as well, by wanting to join my church because of the earthly love for a woman. I grant you that you love your wife very deeply. But this love is but a grain of sand as compared to love for God. I know you cannot be sincere in what you say. I'm going to ask you a direct question. Can you honestly tell me that you no longer believe in the Catholic faith?"

Papa shook his head. "You are a very wise man, Bishop Aden. Thank you."

Bishop Aden placed his hand on Papa's shoulder. "Because I know you to be a God-fearing, righteous and just man; because I know you are incapable of intolerance; I shall speak with candor. Time will heal the wounds of all racial and religious intolerance. The tears men shed because of their intolerance will fall like raindrops upon man's garden of Eden, from which the seeds of true brotherhood shall eventually take root and bloom in every man's garden, regardless of race, color or creed. You will find a way to reconcile your marriage and religion. You will find a way, Tom Fitzgerald, with God's help. And now, good night."

Papa stood staring at the broad back of the tall, gaunt

man, and drew strength and courage from his words. He believed that the good in man must outweigh the evil or there would be no purpose to life. He believed that one day the faces of all men would truly mirror their thoughts and the tongues of all men would truly be the echo of their hearts. That some day all men would realize they were God's children and when they hurt by word or deed another man, they were hurting God.

While on their honeymoon in Denver Papa had asked Mamma if she wanted to go to a Mormon church. She shook her head. "I don't know if there is one here. Let us forget it for the present."

Religion had never been mentioned again until the Sunday following Papa's talk with Bishop Aden. The day had been spent with Papa writing and reading while Mamma was sewing and cooking. After supper, Papa smoked his usual cigar. When he put it out in an ash tray, he walked to the bookcase and removed from it the Douay Bible he'd brought with him from Pennsylvania. Mamma put down the wooden hoops holding the embroidery work she was doing.

"Tena girl," he said, "please get the Book of Mormon I had Mark buy for me the other day." He sat down in his rocking chair until she'd got the book and sat with it in her lap. "I had a talk with Bishop Aden, my dear. A very wise man, the Bishop. He told me that with God's help we will find a way to reconcile our marriage and our religion. We both long for the solace and comfort of spiritual help. Every Sunday evening, I shall read aloud a chapter from my Bible and you shall read aloud to me a chapter from the Book of

Mormon. We will blend our faiths together somehow, with God's help."

After they'd finished reading, they placed the books on the mantel and knelt before it. Papa took his beads from his pocket, and said the Rosary aloud. They remained kneeling while both offered a silent prayer asking God to show them the way.

When they got to their feet, Papa said, "Each night we shall kneel in our bedroom and say the Lord's Prayer together. The Catholic version is different from the one you know. I shall learn your way of saying it."

Mamma smiled at him. "Tom dear, this evening has been wonderful. I feel as if a big emptiness inside of me has gone. Let us also learn each other's hymns. I've wanted to sing a hymn for so long."

"Why not now, Tena girl?" he asked.

"I only know the Latter-Day Saint hymns."

"Then teach me the words, darling."

Mamma walked to the piano. "We'll start with one of the greatest of Mormon hymns," she said as she seated herself. "It is called, 'O My Father.' It has in it one of the doctrines of our religion that we lived in a spiritual world before we were born on this earth."

She struck a chord on the piano and her sweet soprano voice filled the room.

> O my Father, Thou that dwellest
> In the high and glorious place!
> When shall I regain Thy presence,
> And again behold Thy face?
> In Thy holy habitation,
> Did my spirit once reside:
> In my first primeval childhood
> Was I nurtured near Thy side.

For a wise and glorious purpose
Thou hast placed me here on earth
And withheld the recollection
Of my former friends and birth:
Yet ofttimes a secret something
Whispered, "You're a stranger here":
And I felt that I had wandered
From a more exalted sphere!

Papa learned many more Latter-Day Saint hymns during the next few weeks. The first Catholic hymn he taught Mamma by humming the melody until she could play it, then writing out the words, was "Lead, Kindly Light," written by the great English prelate, Cardinal Newman, a convert to Catholicism.

So it came to pass in the town of Adenville, Utah Territory, in the year 1885, that the spiritual hungry among the neighboring Gentile town of Silverlode began making pilgrimages to the Fitzgerald home every Sunday evening. They came first, timid and embarrassed, even apologetic, and remained to sing praises to their God in loud and clear voices. Mark Trainor was among the first. He brought a Latter-Day Saint hymnal at Mamma's request. Judge Baker gave up drinking on Sunday after finding a Methodist hymnal among his dusty law books. Dave Powell dug into his battered trunk and found a Baptist hymnal. Ma Burke, who ran the boarding house, kept hunting among the many boxes, trunks and crates in her home until she found some Catholic hymns. Every Sunday evening the voices of Catholic, Mormon, Methodist and Baptist were raised to sing hymns of all denominations. This community of spiritual singing was made complete the Sunday evening Abe Glassman knocked at the door of the little adobe house.

He was wearing his skull cap, and his bearded face showed how flustered he was, but his small chin jutted with determination. "My good friend," he said, "I have spent many Sunday evenings by the ditch listening to you all. Could I impose on your good wife to play something for me?" His eyes pleaded behind the thick lenses of the spectacles he wore.

Mamma joined Papa at the door. "Do come in, Mister Glassman," she said.

He handed her a book containing Jewish Psalters and hymns, and asked that she play any of them. While Mamma played, Abe listened with tears streaming down his face.

Mamma called him to her side. "I'm going to play it again, Mister Glassman. Please sing the words for us."

Despite his years, Abe's voice was sweet and soft as he sang the words to the Psalter. When he'd finished, Mamma took his hand. "You must teach me the words in your language some day, Mister Glassman, and tell me what they mean. There is so much sadness and loneliness in the music. The meaning of the words must be beautiful."

Abe pressed her hand to his lips. And while the others sang some more hymns, he sat in a chair rocking back and forth with tears falling gently down his cheeks.

Uncle Will never attended these Sunday evenings. He came for Sunday dinner once in a while, but never remained. Unless business at the Whitehorse prevented it, he came almost regularly every Wednesday evening for supper. He usually brought Mamma some expensive gift, but the best presents of all were the copies of sheet music he'd get from Salt Lake City. He had a preference for Irish ballads, and every Wednesday evening the windows of the Mormon neighbors were left open while they listened to solos, duets and very often a trio of voices singing Irish songs. And that was how it happened that the Mormon kids of Adenville were perhaps the only Mormon kids in the Territory who went around whistling Irish ballads.

The first Easter Sunday in their home, the walls of the adobe house rang with the sound of many voices singing hymns of all denominations. Judge Baker rendered a solo of "Jesus Lover of My Soul," the hymn Charles Wesley sang while his brother John preached and laid the foundation for Methodism. Abe Glassman read David's Psalm. Papa sang "Ave Maria." Mamma and Mark Trainor sang "Come Ye Saints," a hymn composed by the Mormons as they crossed the plains to Utah Territory in 1848. Dave Powell sang the beautiful Baptist hymn, "I Know That My Redeemer Lives." They all joined in singing the last hymn, "Praise God From Whom All Blessings Flow."

That night Mamma nestled her head on Papa's shoulder after they had retired. "I love you, Tom dear, with every breath I breathe. There's only been one thing keeping our love from being complete. And now God has given us that very precious thing."

He drew her close to him. "And what is that, my darling?"

"A child," she whispered, "our child shall bind us for all time together. Now our love can never be broken."

The next few months were hectic ones for Papa. He came home one evening when Mamma was six months pregnant and found her in the bedroom, crying. When he tried to comfort her, she pushed him away. To his astonishment she cried out, "Don't touch me!"

Greatly upset, Papa went to the Whitehorse Saloon, where he found Doc Tethers partially sober and told him the incident. Doc coughed blood into a handkerchief. "A pregnant woman becomes very irrational at times," he said. "Your wife will probably be perfectly normal when you return."

Mamma met Papa at the door. "Please forgive me for what I said. I just felt out of sorts."

As Mamma's time drew near, Papa begged her to let him take her to Salt Lake City where she could be hospitalized.

"No," Mamma said firmly. "Our child was conceived in this house, and here he shall be born. Don't worry, Tom dear, we Neilsen women never lose our children."

"But I do worry, Tena girl. Doc Tethers is the only doctor around here and he might be drunk when you need him."

Mamma shook her head.

Two weeks before the baby was born, Papa went through a night of torture. Mamma had barely spoken to him all evening. About midnight he awoke and heard Mamma crying softly into her pillow. He put his arm around her. "What is it, my darling?"

Mamma threw his arm off. "Don't touch me," she cried piteously.

"Tena, my dear, you must tell me why you are crying," he said firmly.

She sat up in bed, her long braids falling over her shoulders. Tears streamed down her face. "I can't. I can't."

For the first time since her pregnancy, Papa became very determined. He put his hands on her shoulders. "You must tell me why you are crying. For the child's sake you must tell me."

Mamma let out a long sobbing moan. "I—I just don't feel really married to you," she wailed.

"But that is ridiculous, Tena girl. We were married twice."

"I know, I know," she cried, "but I still don't feel married to you. The Saints are sealed and married in their Temples for eternity and we—we are only married until death do us part."

Poor Papa couldn't think of a reassuring answer. He lay awake long after Mamma had fallen asleep from exhaustion.

The next morning when he left the house, Papa turned toward Adenville instead of Silverlode. He knew he would find Bishop Aden at the Latter-Day Saints' storehouse. He never could get over marveling at the capacity for work all Mormons seemed to have; in addition to his church duties, Bishop Aden worked his farm and put in long hours every day in the storehouse, in a small office behind a desk piled high with ledgers.

Bishop Aden laid aside his quill pen and motioned for Papa to sit down. "Your face shows loss of sleep, and worry," he said.

Papa took a deep breath. "You told me once that time would heal the wounds of all religious intolerance. I know you were speaking in terms of centuries. But I must bridge that gap within hours. I need your help desperately, sir."

Bishop Aden nodded. "If what you ask is good, then the good Lord will provide a way."

Papa looked into the gentle eyes and somber face. "Tena and I were married in Salt Lake City, and again in Denver after her eighteenth birthday. I swear to you that our marriage vows were not consummated until after the second ceremony. My wife is now pregnant. I can only assume her condition has induced a strange feeling about our marriage. How—how can I explain it so you'll understand?" He shrugged helplessly.

Bishop Aden pulled at the stub of the lobe of his ear with a near smile on his lips. "You're trying to tell me that now your wife is pregnant, she doesn't feel really married to you."

Papa gasped. "How—how did you know?"

"It has happened to other Saints who became apostates. Even a love such as you have for your wife, and her love for you, cannot so quickly undo the teachings and faith of many years."

"Then, sir," Papa pleaded, "you will understand why you must help me. You must let me join the Latter-Day Saints so we can be married as the Mormons are married—for eternity, I believe Tena said."

Bishop Aden clasped his hands in his lap. "I could make great capital out of your conversion. But my answer is the same now as it was that night you asked the same question. What you ask is impossible."

"I was afraid you would say that," Papa slowly shook his head, then raising it, "but can't you marry us in the Mormon faith anyway? Isn't it possible to be married in your faith although one does not belong to your church? You said that if what I wanted was good, the Lord would provide a way. Surely, the happiness and peace of mind of a pregnant woman is such."

Bishop Aden stood up. "I believe what you ask is good, Tom Fitzgerald. You can't be married in our Temple ceremony, but I can marry you in your home. I can also enter the marriage into the church records as being performed the evening of the day you moved into the adobe house so that no one can ever say anything about the child. I'll have Judge Potter execute the license as of that date. Have two trustworthy witnesses at your house at eight o'clock this evening." Bishop Aden raised his face toward the ceiling. "Lord, forgive me if what I do is wrong, but I can see no wrong, but only good in what I am about to do."

Papa grasped the Bishop's hand. "God bless you, sir."

And so, on October 5, 1885, in the presence of Mark Trainor and Dave Powell, Papa and Mamma were married for the third time.

A few nights later, Papa was again awakened by Mamma crying. He pretended to be asleep as he heard her repeat, over and over again, the word "Mother."

The next day he hired a two-seated buggy and team from Tanner's Livery Stable. He drove to Enoch and waited impatiently at the livery stable there while the team was watered, fed and rubbed down. Then, ignoring the peering eyes behind curtained windows, he drove boldly up to Grandpa Swyen's house. He tied the team to a hitching post and walked to the front door.

Grandma Elizabeth opened the door but did not invite him to enter.

He removed his hat. Tears came into his eyes as he groped for words. "You are Tena's mother. You must love her even though she married me. Every night she cries for you. I know nothing about the tenets of your faith. I only know your daughter's child is almost due, and she cries for her mother. Surely God in His infinite mercy would not bless a religion that denies a daughter her mother at a time like this. I beg you to come, comfort and help her."

Grandma Elizabeth's face dimpled as she smiled. "Come in, son, and have a glass of milk and some refreshments while I get ready."

"God bless you," Papa said gratefully. He followed her through the parlor and into the big kitchen. He sat down at a cleanly scrubbed white pine table, while she prepared him a cold mutton sandwich. From a pantry that led off the kitchen she brought a pitcher of milk drawn from a big crock jug, and a piece of cherry pie.

He had just finished eating when she returned with a woman she introduced as Mrs. Fausett. "Sister Maude will accompany us," Grandma Elizabeth said. "She is a midwife."

When they were all seated in the buggy, Grandma Elizabeth said, "Stop at the store, son, so I can tell Tena's father where we are going."

"But," Papa protested, "he might try to stop you."

Grandma Elizabeth said sternly. "Don't ever think a thing like that of Tena's father."

Neighbors had already advised Grandpa Swyen of Papa's visit. He was waiting in front of the store when they drove up. He placed his hand on the buggy wheel and looked anxiously at his wife. "Is Tena ill?"

Grandma Elizabeth smiled. "No more ill than I was when I was carrying her. I'm going to her and taking Sister Maude with me. We'll stay until the baby is born and for as long after as Tena needs us. I know you will give your permission."

Tears came into Grandpa Sweyn's eyes. "Of course, and also my blessing."

Papa leaned down and whispered. "Thank you, sir."

The next day, the 21st of October, 1885, a son was born in the adobe house who was named Sweyn Dennis Fitzgerald, and whose lusty howls kept his parents and neighbors awake for many a night.

*Mamma and Papa
at the time of their
marriage.*

Grandma Neilsen

Grandma Fitzgerald

Grandpa Neilsen

Uncle Will

Grandpa Fitzgerald

Aunt Cathie

(Above) *Our home: Papa (on porch), Mamma, John, Katie, Earnie, Sweyn, Tom.*

(At left) *We children: Tom Dennis, Sweyn Dennis, Katie, John Dennis.*

11

THE BARRIERS BEGIN TO FALL

The birth of Sweyn Dennis brought a complete reconciliation between Papa, Mamma, Grandpa and Grandma Neilsen. They visited each other every few weeks and on holidays. Papa and Mamma took Sweyn Dennis to Salt Lake City when he was three months old to be baptized in the Catholic church.

The subject of religion was never discussed by Papa and Grandpa Sweyn until several months later, when they were in the living room of the adobe house waiting for Mamma and Grandma Elizabeth to finish washing the dishes.

"Go ahead and smoke, Tom," Grandpa said. "Why do you always wait for me to tell you in your own home? I prefer seeing you smoke to seeing you so nervous."

"Thanks," Papa said as he removed a cigar from his pocket and lit it. "It's a habit, I guess, but I do get nervous if I don't have my after-dinner cigar."

Grandpa looked down at the cradle beside the rocking chair. "The little fellow is asleep. He takes after his mother more than you, Tom. He is going to be small like the Neilsens instead of a six-footer like the Fitzgeralds." He turned and looked at Papa. "I know about the Bible reading and

[145]

the singing of hymns on Sunday. I know you and Tena both say your prayers at night. But a child needs religious training. There is an old saying among the Saints that the children of all apostates become infidels. I do not subscribe to this. However, since there is no Catholic church in Adenville, would you have any objection to the boy attending Mormon Primary and Sunday School? I believe all children should attend Sunday school. It gives them a moral and spiritual background which the home cannot provide."

Papa puffed on his cigar for a moment. "I promised Tena that if no Catholic church was available we would send Sweyn Dennis to the Mormon Primary and later to Sunday school. I also promised Tena that if no Catholic church was available when the boy reaches the age of eight, we would have him baptized a Mormon. However, we have both agreed that all our children shall individually choose their own religion when they reach an age where such a decision can be made."

Grandpa Sweyn nodded approval. "We Saints do not teach religion as such to our children until they reach the age of reason, when they are baptized. The Primary Sweyn Dennis would attend is devoted to reading Bible stories, teaching the children how to dance, how to play games, and handicrafts."

The discussion was interrupted by Grandma Elizabeth and Mamma. Grandma walked over to the sleeping child. Unashamed, she pushed her wig to the back of her head and wiped the perspiration from it with a handkerchief. Then turning to where Mamma was sitting with Papa on the sofa, she said, "Why don't you primp up, Tena, and make Tom take you to the dance at the social hall in the Tabernacle?"

Mamma shook her head. "Please, Mother, it would only embarrass everyone including Tom and me."

Grandma gently rocked the cradle as the baby stirred. "It isn't good for you to sit home all the time. You are both still very young. The only decent entertainment is at the church dances and socials. Now, both of you get dressed and go have a good time. Your father and I will take care of the baby until you return. I'll have your father walk over to the Sorsens and tell them we won't be there until after the dance."

"But Mother—" Tena started to protest.

"Do as your mother says," Grandpa spoke up.

Papa was doubtful. "I'm sorry, sir, but I don't—"

Grandpa held up his hand. "I love my daughter, Tom, and I respect you. Nothing will happen to embarrass either of you. I spoke to Bishop Aden about it this afternoon. However," he looked at Tena, "I must caution you that admitting you and Tom to their dances and socials doesn't mean the Saints will invite you into their homes."

Papa held out his hand to Mamma. "Let's do it, Tena girl. If you only knew how wretched I've felt because I haven't been able to take you anywhere but on buggy rides or picnics."

Papa found himself humming as he dressed. He admired Mamma's taste in choosing a plain dress which wouldn't be out of place among the homemade dresses the other women would be wearing. As they walked hand in hand toward the Tabernacle, Mamma squeezed his hand. "No matter what happens tonight, Tom dear, I shall never regret having married you, and will always be happy as long as I have you to love."

The recreation hall of the Tabernacle was in a semi-basement. They could hear the music of the five-piece orchestra as they went down the steps. The hall had benches running around three sides. Bales of hay had been dragged over the floor to make it slick. Couples of all ages were dancing. Papa paid the twenty-five cent admission fee to an Elder of the church sitting near the doorway with baskets of eggs, fruit, and vegetables surrounding him, which had been used for admission by some of the dancers.

Papa and Mamma stood watching the dancers. First one, then another and another couple stopped dancing and stared at them. The orchestra following the gaze of the dancers also stopped playing. Papa saw Bishop Aden pushing his way to the orchestra platform. He saw the Bishop speak to the violinist. The musicians began playing a waltz. Bishop Aden walked toward Papa and Mamma.

Papa felt Mamma's hand trembling on his arm. "We shouldn't have come, dear," she whispered.

Papa threw back his shoulders. "If he asks us to leave, I'll denounce him on the spot."

Bishop Aden stopped in front of Mamma and smiled. "May I have the pleasure, Sister Fitzgerald?"

A dimpled smile wreathed Mamma's face. And as he swept her onto the dance floor she whispered to him, "God bless you."

The Bishop's action seemed to be a general signal for the men to approach Papa. They greeted him warmly. When the waltz was over, Bishop Aden brought Mamma back, but claimed the very next waltz. Then he mounted the platform and began calling a square dance, and Papa and Mamma accepted the smiling invitation of a set of dancers to join their group. During the evening, Papa danced with several of the Mormon women present. Poor Papa got only two dances all evening with Mamma because she was the belle of the ball.

The dance ended with the playing of "Home, Sweet Home." Bishop Aden mounted the platform. Papa and

Mamma, knowing the Saints always opened and closed these dances with a prayer, bowed their heads.

"Oh Lord," Bishop Aden prayed in a solemn voice, "we thank Thee for permitting us this evening of wholesome entertainment as we háve always thanked Thee in the past. We also thank Thee for having blessed us one and all with understanding and tolerance. May we continue to exemplify these virtues and Thy commandments. Please see us each safely home. I ask these blessings in Thy name. Amen."

As Papa and Mamma walked home, both felt a happiness they could not put into words. They knew they would be welcome at future dances and socials, and they knew that Mamma could start trading at the general store in Adenville. They knew the Mormon farmers would stop at Mamma's home and sell her their produce, and they knew the Mormons would pass the time of day with them when they met.

They also knew that no Mormon women would call on Mamma or invite her into their homes. They knew that there would be a few Mormons whose intolerant fanaticism would force them to make it as difficult as possible for Mamma. But at least, the barriers had begun to fall.

12

Silverlode began dying one night in the Whitehorse Saloon when a miner named Paul Brinker, who was quite drunk, slammed his fist on the bar and shouted, "I'm gittin' out. Yessiree, I'm gittin' out of this camp. Four men in a week killed by slides and cave-ins. I hear they've hit water at the Pair-O-Deuces. This town is done for. The silver will peter out and what's left won't be worth pumping the water out to get."

Papa, who published the ore shipments each week in *The Advocate* from figures given him by the stamping mill, had noticed a steady decline in production for some time. He saw Paul Brinker's prediction begin to come true two months later when the Pair-O-Deuces mine was closed. Three months later the miners at the Corry mine went on strike for new safety regulations as the number of men being killed and crippled increased alarmingly. Those were days when eastern capitalists demanded fantastic returns on their investments; their answer to the miners' demands was to close the Corry down. The exodus of miners, muckers, gamblers and dance hall girls from Silverlode began.

Within less than a year there was only the original Silverlode mine in operation. The population of the town had decreased from five thousand to five hundred people. Papa was in *The Advocate* office the day Dale Ferrin, Mine Superintendent for the Silverlode Mining and Development Corporation, entered to order printed notices that the Silverlode mine would cease all operations on September 16, 1886.

The day the mine closed, Papa sat at his roll-top desk with his green eyeshade pushed back on his curly black hair. His hand trembled as he dipped a quill pen into an inkwell. This was to be the hardest editorial he'd ever written. There was so much that had to be left unsaid: there was Mamma pregnant with another child almost due; there was the new and bigger house he'd been planning on building, now just an empty dream; there was the stark reality that he could not support himself and his family with only Mormon subscribers. There was the certainty that he could not obtain employment on any other newspaper in the Territory because they were all either pro- or anti-Mormon, and even he could not bring himself to prostitute his convictions even for his family. The fact that he'd never received a single letter from his brother John or his sisters in Pennsylvania ruled out any possibility of going back home. And intertwined with every possible solution was the death-bed promise he'd made his mother always to look out for his brother.

The last edition of *The Silverlode Advocate* contained no advertising. It consisted of a single sheet printed on both sides containing the following editorial:

IN AT THE DEATH

When a man dies, there is always at least one friend or loved one who mourns his passing. If he dies without friends or loved ones, there is always one charitable person who can be called upon to say a few good words for the deceased. When a town dies, there is not one who mourns for the town itself. Its citizens mourn only with self-pity because the death of the town has taken from them personally a legitimate, illegitimate, moral or immoral livelihood.

When the fabulous Pair-O-Deuces mine closed, men talked only of what the closing meant to them personally. Not one mourned for the town of Silverlode, which lost more than a thousand citizens when the mine closed. Men talked only of the $34,000,000.00 in horn silver that had been ripped from the earth leaving a scar 850 feet long, 325 feet wide and 740 feet deep.

When the Corry mine closed men talked only of the horn silver the mine produced, yielding more than a hundred dollars a ton. Not one mourned that another integral part of Silverlode had been lost, with a decrease in her population of several hundred.

The closing of the Mule's Ear, the Bonanza and the Tinker reduced the population of Silverlode to less than five hundred people. With the closing of the Silverlode, the original strike which outlasted all others and from which almost $450,000,000.00 of horn silver was taken, leaving a hole 1,000 feet long, 500 feet wide and 900 feet deep, the last artery was severed and Silverlode quickly bled to death.

I have just walked the length and breadth of a ghost town. Dogs abandoned by their owners are already becoming wild and running in packs ready to join the wolves and coyotes. Mother Nature is struggling to cover with vegetation the scars left by men in their lust for wealth. The sun beats down, the wind blows, and all the elements seem to conspire to destroy the empty buildings and all evidence that men once lived here.

A town dies hard and extracts a terrible price from those who did it to death. Did the wealth that men pillaged from the earth bring them happiness? Hundreds of miners died from miner's con. Hundreds of miners died in accidents. Hundreds of miners were crippled and maimed. Hundreds of men were murdered. Thousands of men were robbed and swindled. Hundreds of women sold their bodies, and mortgaged their souls to the devil.

There are those, Gentile and Latter-Day Saint alike, who opposed Brigham Young's edict against mining. Perhaps Brigham Young could see what other men did not, until it was too late. Just a stone's throw from the ghost town of Silverlode lies Adenville, where men have nurtured Mother Earth instead of abusing her. Adenville is secure and prosperous because men were wise. From her farming, her agricultural produce, her cattle and sheep raising, her industries, Adenville remains, and in the fullness of time will outproduce the wealth of all the mines in Silverlode.

To be in on the death of Silverlode is doubly hard for your editor. For more than a town has died here. A dream has died. A dream that one newspaper in the Utah Territory would uphold the integrity of impartial reporting of events affecting the lives of both Mormons and Gentiles. I am proud *The Advocate* never missed a single edition. I am grateful to my subscribers for accepting without complaint the numerous editions printed on inferior paper and wrapping paper when newsprint was impossible to obtain.

With this last edition of *The Silverlode Advocate,* I wish to express my gratitude to my subscribers, advertisers and printing customers for their loyal support. All money due subscribers whose subscriptions haven't expired can be had by calling at *The Advocate* office, or will be refunded in person by your editor.

I have tried to be a friend to all men worthy of friendship. I have tried to be a credit to the fourth estate. If I have failed any man, or written a single sentence that was detrimental to journalism, I have done so unknowingly.

Silverlode is dead. *The Silverlode Advocate* is dead. I put my newspaper to bed for the last time. But man lives on. I face the future with confidence because this is America where an equal opportunity for men of all crafts, all races, all creeds will always be found.

> Editorially yours,
> *Tom D. Fitzgerald*

Papa helped Dave Powell set up the type for the last edition of *The Silverlode Advocate,* and watched for a little while as Powell began running the paper through the press. He removed the green eyeshade and his apron. "Dave," he said, "I just can't stand it. Our last edition. I'm going over to see my brother. I'll be back later."

Horseshoe Jim, the bartender, was in back of the bar in the Whitehorse Saloon. His toupee was pushed back on his head; he was mechanically polishing already clean glasses. Barnaby Smith sat at the piano, his derby hat on the side of his head, his fingers gently strumming the keys.

The only other persons in the place were clustered around the big stake poker table. Uncle Will was idly shuffling a deck of cards, Queenie behind him with her hand resting on his shoulder. Judge Baker was scratching his porous red nose. Hal Gentry was polishing one of his guns with a chamois. Dandy Allen and his girl Marie were playing a game with large kitchen matches to see who could build the highest pile by laying them in a triangle on top of one another. Windy Davis was sprawled in a chair, his head tilted back, snoring drunkenly. Doc Tethers was the only one drinking, a bottle in front of him and a glass, which he kept refilling. The hunchback Peter stood in back of Doc watching him.

Uncle Will slammed the deck of cards on the table and leaned back in his chair, hooking his thumbs into the belt of his jeweled holster. "Welcome to the wake," he said to his brother.

Papa pulled a chair up to the table and sat upon it backwards with his arms resting on the back of the chair.

Doc Tethers went into a coughing spell. When he withdrew his handkerchief from his mouth, it was red with blood.

Hal Gentry rubbed his nose with the barrel of his gun. "You oughta hit out for where it's high and dry," he said.

Doc was drunk. "My destination after leaving this Sodom

and Gomorrah is of no concern to anybody but myself." His thin lips curled. "Before I leave you, I wish to express the absolute loathing and contempt I have for each of you. I question the existence of a God who would give straight backs and normal minds to gamblers, murderers, cheats and prostitutes, while denying them to a child born to the purple. If this be God's will, then I say with Schopenhauer that the way to outwit such a cruel God is to have man efface himself from the face of the earth by castrating every living male. I have hated you individually and collectively, and I see no reason for changing at this final parting."

He got up from the table. His voice was gentle as he turned to the hunchback. "Come, Peter, we are going home."

Dandy Allen watched the retreating forms of Doc and the hunchback. "Why have we taken it all these years? Why hasn't somebody killed him?"

Uncle Will shrugged. "Doc has been trying to goad somebody into killing him since he came here. Now, he'll have to do it himself."

Papa leaned forward. "What do you mean by that?"

Uncle Will ran a finger over his mustache. "Doc is broke. Has been for about three months. I used to cash a check that came for him every month from a New York bank. The last one I cashed was three months ago. Since then, Doc has been charging his bar bills here, and his own and the hunchback's meals in the cafes around town." Uncle Will smiled cynically. "We should be hearing shots any minute."

Papa jumped to his feet. "We can't let him do such a thing. It's unchristian."

"Tom," Uncle Will said slowly, "I told you when you first came here that the surest way to make enemies was to try and live somebody else's life."

As he finished speaking, a shot rang out, and a moment later another.

Uncle Will signaled for Horseshoe Jim to bring glasses and a bottle. "It is better this way," he said as he poured a drink around. "Doc might have died any minute from consumption and the hunchback would have to be sent to an institution." He raised his glass. "To Doc Tethers. At last he is through running away."

They found the hunchback lying on the floor with his arms folded. Doc was seated at the desk in his office, his body thrown back in the chair. He'd placed the gun in his mouth and pulled the trigger. A strong box lay on the desk and a note on it. Papa picked up the note, it read in part:

Mr. Tom Fitzgerald:
Because I dislike you less than any other man in Silverlode, I address this last request to you. Give my surgical instruments to any hospital of your choosing. Give my library to any college of your choosing. Bury my son and me in a common grave. Place no headstone upon it. Let Mother Earth cover us and remove any trace that we ever inhabited this planet. I do now what I lacked the courage to do many years ago.
I subscribe myself,
Dr. Frederic Tethers Crumbler.

Papa read the note aloud and then looked around the room. "The details of Doc's past are in this strong box. We have no right to pry into it. We guessed right that the hunchback Peter was his son. We'll bury his secret with him."

When they returned to the Whitehorse Saloon, they again sat down around the big stake poker table. Papa looked across it at Uncle Will. "Where will you go?" he asked.

Uncle Will shook his head. "Won't know until Butch Mears gets back. Butch freighted the 66 down to Needles.

Want to hear what he thinks of the place. I'll let you know, Tom." He looked around the table at Gentry, Baker, Windy Davis, Dandy Allen and the two girls. "Where I go, they go."

Mark Trainor entered as Uncle Will finished speaking. Uncle Will turned to Hal Gentry. "The night Kid O'Toole drew on this Mormon, I made up my mind that I'd never go up against Trainor. He's the fastest man on the draw I ever saw."

Papa dropped his voice to a whisper as Mark approached. "Mark is no gunman. He was forced into drawing against the three men he killed." He turned in his chair. "Hello, Mark."

Mark stood relaxed with his hat pushed back over his sandy-colored hair. "I want to talk to you, Tom."

Papa got up. "I was just leaving. Going back to *The Advocate* office."

Uncle Will called after them. "You're both invited to the wake tonight. I'm throwing a free banquet and free drinks for everybody left in Silverlode."

Mark didn't speak until they reached *The Advocate* office. "Dave Powell left, Tom, right after he finished printing that last edition. He caught a ride with the Clemson brothers to Salt Lake. Said you'd understand."

Papa pushed open the doors of the office. "Dave knew it would be hard for me to say goodbye." He walked over to where Powell had neatly stacked the last edition of *The Silverlode Advocate*. "This is going to take some time. I must personally deliver these and at the same time refund money to most of the subscribers."

"I'll help you," Mark volunteered. "But tomorrow will do. The Mormons aren't leaving and all your Gentile subscribers have gone. Tom, I took a copy of this issue of *The Advocate* to Bishop Aden. He read it and then said to me.

'Tom Fitzgerald can't leave Adenville. It doesn't fit in with my plans.' "

Papa smiled. "The Bishop is a good man, but he knows I couldn't accept charity."

Mark looked into Papa's eyes. "Would you say I'm the type of a person who would accept charity?"

Papa shook his head. "Of course not, Mark."

"I promised Bishop Aden this morning that I would become Sheriff next week. Jeffers is buying a farm."

"But Mark, they don't need a sheriff or a marshal now that Silverlode is dead."

"Not right now, Tom, but they will soon. That is what Bishop Aden wants to talk to you about."

They walked to the Bishop's home and were admitted into the parlor. Bishop Aden was seated at a small cabinet desk. He stood up and held out his hand.

"It was good of you to come."

Papa shook hands and sat down in a straight-backed chair. Bishop Aden seated himself and began pulling at the stub of his ear. "The railway is coming to Adenville, Tom," he announced. Without waiting for Papa to recover his surprise, the Bishop continued: "The church has acquired a right-of-way and will build the railway with church funds. The right-of-way will run from Salt Lake City to Prater, and from Prater down this side of the range to Adenville."

"But that is impossible," Papa said.

"I know what you are thinking," Bishop Aden smiled, "but our engineers say that it is no more impossible to take the railway up over Frazer Pass than it was for the Denver and Rio Grande to build a railway over Soldier Summit."

Papa was still skeptical. "Assuming it can be done, sir, there isn't enough industry and agriculture to support a railway."

Bishop Aden made a tent with his hands on the desk. "It is estimated that seven-eighths of what will one day be the state of Utah has coal beneath it. Just a few miles north of Enoch there is a valley with a vein of coal which runs beneath the mountain for miles. Five other potential sites for mines have been leased or sold to eastern capitalists who will develop the mines. That brings the railway as far as Enoch, almost. We are going to bring in thousands of head of sheep and cattle. We have the grazing land in this area as you are aware. We are going to build up our industries and triple our production of agriculture. We are going to make Adenville the railway terminal, complete with roundhouse and repair shops."

Again Papa shook his head. "It will require a lot of capital. I don't mean for the railway. That has been taken care of by the church as you pointed out. I am referring to the increase in industry and agriculture and the bringing in of sheep and cattle."

Bishop Aden nodded. "Considerably more than we Saints in Dixie possess, but the church will back the venture. We are going to charter a bank. We know your brother to be a wealthy man. My first proposition is to him. I will not pretend that I have any personal liking for your brother, nor he for me. But I will say that we Saints are realistic enough to know that with the coming of the railway, the coming of big herds of sheep and cattle, the coming of the nearby coal mines, the peculiar brand of entertainment your brother can provide will be a necessity. We prefer to have a man we know will keep himself and his kind of people in their place. We know that he, Marshal Gentry, and Judge Baker have the power and the courage to keep law and order. We know they will discourage any attempts by the rougher elements of East Adenville to invade West Adenville."

Papa shrugged helplessly. "You are ahead of me. What do you mean by East and West Adenville?"

"The railway will bisect what is now the Jensen farm," Bishop Aden elaborated. "We will sell your brother any property for the purposes of speculation or to build upon on the east side of those tracks. This will permit him to construct his saloon near the loading pens, the sheep-shearing pens and the roundhouse. We will set forth the same conditions between the two towns as existed between Silverlode and Adenville. We will also permit your brother to operate a tent saloon and gambling hall along the right-of-way during the construction of the railway. For and in consideration of all these things, we ask that your brother purchase twenty-five thousand dollars in shares in our bank."

Papa thought for a moment. "I'll have to speak to him about it, Bishop Aden."

"It would suit us Mormons individually and collectively if we could remain aloof, but that is impossible. We've no right to stand in the way of progress or to do anything which may stand in the way of Utah becoming a state. We Saints know that it will be Gentiles of your caliber who will help us toward statehood. We know that journalists of your ability and integrity will help to carry the true story of Mormonism to the ears of those who have heard only the worst about us. I realize that we cannot support a newspaper at the present time. But with the coming of the coal mines, the railway, the sheep and the cattle, we will need a newspaper. We wish to assure ourselves that when the time arrives, we will have a newspaper edited by a man of integrity like yourself. Until such a time, we wish to offer you a position in our newly organized bank as a cashier. There is no charity in this offer, Tom, and you know that we need you far more than you need us. Just as men like your brother have a place in the scheme of things that will one day make Utah a great state, so too, do men like yourself have a far greater responsibility. Will you do it for us, Tom? Will you do it for me? For as surely as the snow covers the mountain peaks each winter, we shall one day be not Mormons and Gentiles, but Utahans."

Papa got to his feet, and looked into Bishop Aden's eyes. "You do me great honor, sir. I pledge my word, my last dollar, my friendship, my talents and my eternal gratitude to you and the Saints."

A few days later, Papa took Mamma for a walk. He showed her the place in West Adenville where they would build their new home. He cupped her chin in his hand. "Tell me, Tena girl, why I can think of a thousand ways to tell you that you are beautiful and yet when I look at you, all I can say is you are beautiful, my darling. Tell me, Tena girl, why I can think of a thousand and one ways in which I love you, and yet when I hold you in my arms, I can only say I love you, my dear. Tell me, Tena girl, why I love you so very, very much and tell you of my love so seldom."

Then, oblivious of any persons who might have been watching, Papa kissed Mamma on the spot where he built the house where I was born.

13

APOSTATE

WHEN PAPA outlined to Uncle Will the proposals made by Bishop Aden, he was agreeably surprised at the readiness with which they were accepted. He had gone directly to the Whitehorse Saloon from the Bishop's home. Uncle Will was holding his wake for the town of Silverlode. There were about fifty persons in the saloon and everyone except Uncle Will and Queenie was quite drunk.

Uncle Will looked across the table at which he was sitting while talking to his brother. "You look surprised, Tom. Do you realize that with a tent saloon and gambling hall, I'll be collecting practically the entire payroll from the men who build the railway? Not only that, it will be a new experience. I'll take Hal Gentry along to keep order, and Judge Baker because I'll need him later when the railway reaches Adenville. I think I'll make Dandy my partner and let him run the gambling games. And I'll take Windy with me because he has no place else to go. Horseshoe Jim and Barnaby Smith go along too. And," Uncle Will looked at Queenie and smiled, "you, my beautiful red-headed doll. The living conditions will be a little rough, but it will be fun."

The next day Papa closed the doors of *The Advocate*

office, and stored his printing press and equipment in an unused granary that Bishop Aden owned. He then began to build an extra bedroom on the adobe house because his second child was almost due. The bedroom was completed just before my sister Katie was born. She was a big baby, inheriting big bones and a large frame from Papa's side of the family. She was just a year younger than Sweyn Dennis, but by the time she was five years old she was as tall as he.

The construction of the bank building was begun. As was the custom in those days, Papa, Bishop Aden and the others all worked on it. Upon its completion, Papa assumed his position as cashier. Papa disliked everything about banking except lending money. Fortunately for him very few of the loans weren't repaid.

When the directors of the bank informed Papa they were ready to put up the money, either as loans, or to form a company, to bring in sheep and cattle, Papa asked them to give him some time to investigate the matter. He had read somewhere that the Basques from Lower Navarre in France were among the best sheepmen in the world. He wrote to the French Embassy in Washington asking them to recommend Basque immigrants, with the bank offering to advance passage money.

That was how Henri Dussiere and his wife came to Adenville. Papa stunned the Frenchman by calmly handing him ten thousand dollars and telling him to go to California and bring back sheep. Also Papa wrote to the editor of a Texas newspaper asking him to recommend a cattle buyer who could bring herds of steers into Utah Territory. That was how Sam Wade came to Adenville. The Texan wasn't surprised when Papa gave him a large amount of money for this purpose.

The banking business proved too confining for Papa.

When he had to refuse a man a loan, he always later sought him out and loaned the money personally. When the construction of the roundhouse was begun, Papa left the banking business and went into the real estate business.

Sheepmen and cattlemen came to East Adenville and built homes there. Papa made enough money from the real estate business to build his new house before his third child, Tom Dennis, Jr., was born.

Mamma's ostracism continued through these years. She and Papa were welcome at the church dances and socials, and the Mormon women stopped to chat with her on the street or when they met at the general store. But the only two Mormon women who invited Mamma into their homes, and visited her in her home, were her next-door neighbors, Mrs. Lillian Smith and Mrs. Sarah Fransen.

Mamma also visited—and the visits were returned by them—the very few Gentile families that moved into East Adenville. If she was lonely she did not betray her loneliness to Papa, but at times her heart ached for him because she knew he would be unhappy until he could go back to journalism. Later she recalled the many times he'd say, "If I were publishing *The Advocate* now, I could do a good editorial on this."

Therefore she rejoiced when the railway reached Castle Rock, the new coal mining camp just a few miles from Enoch. Papa made a trip to Castle Rock and the three coal mining camps above it, remaining overnight at Grandpa Sweyn's in Enoch. When he returned he had enough commitments for subscriptions, advertising and printing, coupled with the business he could get in East and West Adenville, to revive *The Advocate*. He bought a small frame building that had formerly housed a creamery on Main Street in West Adenville, and got his printing press and equipment from the granary. When the presses were ready to roll he wrote his first editorial for the newly named *Adenville Advocate* and in it portrayed his joy at being back in journalism.

DREAMS DO COME TRUE

There were men of vision who dreamed they could build a railway where skeptics said one could not be built. The doubters kept saying, "Wait until they reach Frazer Pass." But these men of vision laid the steel rails to the summit of Frazer Pass with a looping double-S curve, and the impossible became a reality.

There were other men of vision who said, "We will bring in sheep from California and cattle from Texas. We will dot the hillsides and valleys and the top of the plateau around Adenville with these herds." And it was done. Shearing pens are now being constructed, and loading pens are already built alongside the right-of-way of the new railway. These men of vision made the dream come true.

Your editor also had a dream. It was a little dream compared to building the railway or making Adenville the livestock center of Dixie. Your editor's dream came true with this first issue of *The Adenville Advocate*.

The men of vision who built the railway to carry the coal to warm the homes and stoke the furnaces of industry are writing history.

The men of vision who brought in the sheep and the cattle to feed and clothe the people of the West are writing history.

Your editor, in all humility, cannot restrain the pride he feels in being privileged to record these historical events in *The Adenville Advocate*.

Editorially yours,
Thomas D. Fitzgerald

Uncle Will began the construction of the new Whitehorse Saloon in East Adenville soon after I was born. The Sheepman's Hotel, the Frontier Hotel, The Prairie Restaurant,

Allies Saloon, a tailor shop, barber shop, saddlery and several other places of business lined the Main Street of East Adenville before the railway reached there.

Mamma's ostracism by the majority of the Mormon women in West Adenville continued until Sweyn Dennis was eight years of age. Grandpa and Grandma Neilsen had driven over from Enoch for Sweyn's birthday. Grandpa reminded Papa of his promise, and Sweyn was baptized a Latter-Day Saint.

It was this simple religious rite that seemed almost completely to break down the barriers of Mamma's ostracism. We children had always gone to the Mormon Primary and the Mormon school, but it wasn't until Sweyn was baptized that the Mormon women began calling on Mamma and inviting her to their homes. They also asked her to join their sewing circle, quilting bees, and other clubs not directly connected with the Mormon church; and they got her to help them coach, produce, and make costumes for the many plays and operettas they presented in the Tabernacle. We children were always given a part in these theatrical productions.

There was a minority of fewer than a dozen Mormon women who still continued to treat Mamma as an apostate. The leader of this group was Old Lady Miller. Somehow, even today, I cannot think of her except as Old Lady Miller. She was a thin, ugly woman with a mustache you could see when close to her. She wore her sparse hair in a scrawny bun at the nape of her neck. Her husband had been killed from the kick of a mule, and there were some people who said that her husband had either coaxed or tormented the mule into kicking him. She was forty years old at the time of her husband's death, but made no effort to support herself, though she owned a small house and, as was customary with the Mormons, the church provided her with sufficient welfare for her needs. She repaid this generosity by becoming the town shrew and scandalmonger. She'd exaggerate a harmless hand-in-hand walk home from a dance into a trip to a haystack. She did have, however, one redeeming feature, her ability to nurse the sick. No one ever had to send for her; she had a power of intuition where illness would strike that was uncanny. People told of the time she showed up at the Olsen home with her black satchel at three o'clock one afternoon. Mrs. Olsen laughingly told her there wasn't anyone ill in her family. Old Lady Miller ignored her and went about fixing up a bed to receive a sick person. At four o'clock that afternoon Mrs. Olsen's husband broke his leg in an accident at the sawmill where he worked, fourteen miles from West Adenville.

Mamma's first personal encounter with Old Lady Miller was the first time she'd been invited to join the sewing circle at a meeting held in Sarah Fransen's home. When Old Lady Miller entered the parlor and saw Mamma sitting with the other ladies, she pointed her finger at Mamma and shouted, "I will not remain in the same house as this immoral, wanton creature."

Sarah Fransen stood up and put her hands on her hips. "Then I suggest you leave. This is my house and Tena is my guest."

Old Lady Miller's persecution of Mamma started the very next day. She spread a story around town that she'd peeked into our dining-room window and seen both Papa and Mamma drunk in front of us children. What she actually saw was Papa having his usual glass of brandy after supper and Mamma drinking some homemade root beer. Poor Mamma never touched a drop of alcohol in her life except for the brandy she put into her fruit cakes.

I was six years old, my brother Tom seven, and my sister

Katie going on nine when I first felt the wrath of Old Lady Miller. We were walking past her house when she was sitting on the porch. She ran to the picket fence across the front of her lawn, shook her fists at us and screamed: "You little infidels will burn in Hades."

My sister Katie got hysterical and ran screeching toward our home. I was ready to take out after her when I saw my brother Tom glaring right back at her. Then he stuck his thumbs in his ears, wiggled his fingers and began shouting, "I'm a crazy little infidel. I'm a crazy little infidel."

Old Lady Miller gathered up her skirts and ran into her house, locking the door behind her. This didn't stop her persecution of Mamma. Old Lady Miller would sneak into our back yard, up on our porch, and suddenly throw open the kitchen door. She'd point her finger at Mamma and scream, "Down on your knees, you wicked woman. Down on your knees and beg the Lord to show you the way back to the true church." Poor Mamma never knew when Old Lady Miller would burst into our house and start screaming imprecations at her.

Papa finally had to get Judge Potter to issue an injunction preventing Old Lady Miller from trespassing on our property, but this didn't stop her from running into the street when Mamma passed, and saying vile things to her.

My brother Tom's great brain finally saved the day. Every year we received a copy of the *World Almanac* as a bonus for Papa renewing his subscription to the *New York World*. Tom spent hours reading the almanacs. He knew everything. Sometimes his teacher would say to him, "Maybe we ought to change places."

One day I came home and found Mamma crying after meeting Old Lady Miller on the street. I went to the barn and called to my brother who was up in the loft. He came down the rope ladder. "T. D.," I said to him (we boys always called each other by our first two initials because that was the way Papa addressed us), "with your great brain can't you figure out a way to get rid of Old Lady Miller? I just saw Mamma, and Old Lady Miller has made her cry again."

My brother had curly hair like Papa. He was built rather on the chunky side and had freckles.

"J. D.," he said seriously, "I'll put my great brain to work at once. Old Lady Miller hasn't got a chance against my great brain."

That night after supper, Tom sat staring into the flames in the natural rock fireplace of our parlor. Papa was sitting in his black leather-upholstered rocker, reading a book. Mamma was sewing. When I think of Mamma, I always think of her hands. They were busy hands, always moving. Sweyn Dennis, Katie and I were playing dominoes.

Tom got up, walked over to Papa, and placed his hand on Papa's knee. "Papa," he asked, "where do they put crazy people?"

Papa laid aside his book. "Why do you ask, T. D.?"

Tom's face was serious. "All the kids say old Alf Peters is crazy. He lives in that shack down by the old camp ground and keeps his two jackasses right in the house with him. He's dirty and never takes a bath. He talks to his two jackasses just like they were people. Don't they have a place where they put crazy people?"

Papa brushed back the cowlick on his forehead. "There are different kinds of crazy people, T. D. Some are just peculiar and harmless like old Alf. He never hurt anyone. He lives in a sort of dream world where all the animals and the birds are the same to him as people. Although he never takes a bath himself, he keeps his two jackasses cleaner than any horses in town. He makes his jackasses happy by talking to them. He makes the birds happy by feeding them in the winter. They say that wild rabbits will eat out of his hand. People say old Alf is crazy, but he probably thinks the same about us."

Tom nodded. "I never threw rocks at old Alf or teased him like some of the kids do. I laugh at him when I see him talking to his two jackasses, but I can't help it. I understand why nobody wants to send old Alf to a place they keep crazy people, but what about the other kind?"

Papa thought for a moment. "Sometimes a person has such a great shock or sorrow that it makes him sick in his mind. Sometimes a disease can make a person sick in his mind. It is difficult to explain, but I will try. Some people who are sick in their minds think that everybody is against them, even the persons who really love them. They believe everybody is trying to hurt them or destroy them. Their sick minds make them strike back. They do everything they can to hurt, and if sick enough, even try to kill the people who really love them and want to help them. There are others who are so sick in their minds they try to commit suicide. These are the type of people who for their own protection and the protection of society must be placed in asylums."

Tom looked Papa in the eye. "Everybody says Old Lady Miller is crazy as a bedbug and she is always trying to hurt somebody. Why don't they put her in an asylum?"

Papa shook his head. "Mrs. Miller never hurt anyone physically, T. D. She has done a lot of good nursing people. She just can't help lying about people. Her only trouble is her tongue. She has never done anything that could be construed as being crazy."

"What does 'construed' mean, Papa?"

" 'Interpreted' is about the same. In other words, T. D.,

Mrs. Miller has never done anything that could be considered abnormal enough to make her appear crazy."

That night after Mamma had tucked Sweyn, Tom and me into bed in the room we all three occupied upstairs, and listened to our prayers, my brother Tom was out of bed as soon as she'd gone back downstairs.

He got Sweyn up. "My great brain has figured out a plan for driving Old Lady Miller plumb crazy."

Sweyn called Tom and me infants sometimes, but whenever the family were involved he'd join a conspiracy as quickly as he'd fight any bigger boys who picked on us.

I was mystified when Tom told me to sneak into the upstairs hallway and get my box of colored crayons. By the light of the moon coming through the window, he painted Sweyn's face like an Indian's before a war dance. He sat in the window while Sweyn made terrible-looking streaks on his face. They both rubbed their bodies with a concoction Tom had made from red clay and water. Then they dressed up in their genuine Indian war bonnets, breech clouts, moccasins, and beaded arm-bands that Uncle Will had given them. They put bowie knives in their teeth and their genuine Indian tomahawks in the strings of their breech clouts. They looked so fierce and real they frightened me.

I was too small to swing from our bedroom window to the limb of the elm tree, so I had to stay behind, but I watched them as they reached the ground. Two of our dogs came around the house growling, but changed their growls to a welcome whimper when they smelled who it was. I saw Tom pick up his stilts—made by nailing blocks of wood on a long piece of wood and using the leather from old shoes for straps.

Tom and Sweyn made their way over a devious route to Old Lady Miller's house, and they stopped beneath her bedroom window several feet from the ground. There was no screen on it, just mosquito netting. Tom let Sweyn stand on his back. Sweyn pushed aside the mosquito netting and crept into the bedroom. He waited until Tom had got on his stilts and had his head and shoulders in the window. At Tom's signal, Sweyn pinched the tail of one of Old Lady Miller's cats which he'd been petting. She always slept with three or four of them in her bedroom. The cat let out a screech.

Sweyn remained on his hands and knees out of sight while Old Lady Miller sat up in bed and struck a match to light the lamp on the bedstand. "Was that you, Susie?" she called to her cat.

Sweyn leaped to his feet and let out an Apache war cry. Waving the tomahawk in one hand and the bowie knife in the other, he did a war dance around the bed, and Tom joined in with a terrifying war whoop. Standing on his stilts, he looked as if he were just crawling in the window. Old Lady Miller must have thought an entire Indian tribe was coming into her bedroom. She made it from the bed to the door in one bound. Her screams could be heard blocks away.

Fred Bowler, who lived across the street from her, was awakened by the screams. He opened his front door just in time to see an apparition come flying out of Mrs. Miller's house, streak across the lawn and jump with ease the fence separating the two houses.

Old Lady Miller was screaming: "Run for your lives. The Indians are attacking. Run for your lives." She kept right on running in her flannel nightgown, leaping fences, until she came to one that was five feet high and made from boards. This one she didn't quite make. She fell, striking her head and knocking herself unconscious.

There was such a commotion going on with dogs barking and men shouting to one another, that I got so frightened I would have run down stairs if I hadn't heard my brothers returning. They had just got back into the bedroom when Mamma called up the stairway asking if we were all right.

Tom answered as if he were half asleep. "Yes, Mamma. Is something wrong? We thought we heard a noise, didn't we, Sweyn?"

"Go to sleep," Sweyn said drowsily.

"J. D. is asleep, Mama," Tom called.

"Don't worry, dears," she called back. "Everything is all right."

Tom and Sweyn quickly undressed and used a flour sack to wipe the paint and crayons from their bodies and faces. Not until they were in bed did they tell me about it. They'd take turns telling of the exploit and we'd stick our heads under the covers, stuff blankets into our mouths, and laugh and laugh.

The next morning I thought to ask if they'd removed all evidence. "Sure, J. D.," Tom said as if he were offended. "I filled up the holes my stilts made and used a branch off a tree to cover up all traces of our feet."

If Old Lady Miller hadn't tripped over that last fence and hurt herself, nothing would have come of my brother's great plan. People might have excused her insistence that she really saw Indians as being due to a nightmare. Her sprained shoulder was still in a bandage when my two brothers made a repeat call upon her a few nights later. This time she ran all the way to Bishop Aden's house screaming, "The Indians are back. Run for your lives."

Before Utah became a state in 1896, in most communities there were only the Mormon courts. These courts were rarely concerned with anything but civil rights. The Bishop and these courts could usually settle any disputes without resorting to the Federal Territory Courts. In West Adenville

Mark Trainor was the Marshal, and Judge Potter sat on the bench. In East Adenville Hal Gentry was Marshal, and Frank Baker, Judge.

It was only a few days after my brothers had paid their second visit to Old Lady Miller that she was taken to court. Judge Potter committed her for observation to the asylum in Provo. The Judge told her he was doing it for her own good because he feared she might hurt herself.

When Tom heard the news, he was jubilant. "My great brain did it. I said I'd drive her plumb crazy and I did."

Old Lady Miller was held in custody in her own house by two Mormon women. The night before Uncle Mark, as all we children called the Marshal, was to take her to Provo on the train, she must finally have realized what was happening to her. Her own Saints had turned against her. Sitting in the parlor of her home fondling one of her cats, she saw no sympathy in the eyes of her jailers. It was perhaps the copy of *The Advocate* that one of the women guards was reading that was father to the desperate thought that came to Old Lady Miller. She excused herself to get a drink of water, went out the back way of her home and ran to our house.

Our whole family were in the parlor when the front door suddenly burst open and Old Lady Miller ran to Papa. She threw herself on her knees, raised her arms and cried out: "Tom Fitzgerald, you're known as a good man, a just man. I beg you to help me. My own people have turned against me. I'm not crazy. I swear before the Lord I saw and heard the Indians right in my very bedroom. Please have mercy on me. Please help me. What will happen to my cats? In the name of Jesus Christ, please help me."

Mamma assisted the old lady to a rocking chair. "I know you hate me, Tena Fitzgerald," Old Lady Miller cried as she seized Mamma's hand and began kissing it. "Please, please ask your husband to help me."

I was surprised to see tears in Mamma's eyes. I thought she should be laughing like all get out. Mamma pressed Old Lady Miller's hand against her breast. "I do not hate you. I have never hated you." Mamma's face became streaked with tears. "If there were anything I could do, or my husband could do, to help you we would. You must believe that."

I was getting all choked up inside. I felt ashamed of the feel of tears in my own eyes. I watched my brother Tom walk over and put his arm around Mamma's waist. He looked up at her. "Why are you crying, Mamma? I thought you'd be happy."

Mamma patted his head. "One must cry when one is sad," she said softly.

Tom's face twisted with doubt. "But Mamma, do you really want to help her after all she's done to you?"

"To forgive is divine, my son."

Tom took a deep breath. He walked over to Papa and placed his hand on Papa's knee. "Do you want to help her too, Papa?"

Papa noded. "Of course, T. D. If there were anything I could do, I would do it."

Tom stood very straight. "If Mrs. Miller could prove she really saw Indians in her bedroom, would that save her?"

A startled expression came over Papa's face. He grabbed Tom by the shoulders. "T. D., if you know anything that might save Mrs. Miller, you must tell me. I promise you that you will not be punished. We must forget the trouble and hurt she has caused us. You must only remember that if you can save her and don't, it will be on your conscience all your life. And you will be twice as evil as you ever believed her to be."

Tom confessed, with Sweyn filling in details when Tom hesitated. When it was over, Papa patted him on the shoulder. "Thank you, T. D. You have prevented a gross miscarriage of justice." He got up and went over to where Old Lady Miller was sitting. "It is we who now beg of you the mercy you sought from us. Can you ever forgive us?"

Old Lady Miller threw her arms around Papa's neck and kissed him right on the lips. Then she hugged and kissed Mamma. I was next, then Katie and Sweyn. I remember the funny look on Tom's face when she hugged and kissed him several times.

It was just at this time Uncle Mark came to our door. Papa invited him in and explained everything. "I want you to release Mrs. Miller in my custody until morning, Mark. She will spend the night here. Evidence will be introduced in Judge Potter's court tomorrow which will prove that Mrs. Miller actually saw and heard what she assumed were Indians in her bedroom."

It was certainly strange to see Old Lady Miller at our breakfast table the next morning. But everything worked out fine for Tom and me. From then on every time we passed her house she'd call us in and give us cookies or homemade candy. Later, Dr. LeRoy said it was only Old Lady Miller's good nursing that pulled my brother Tom through when he got diphtheria.

14

BERTHA TUTTLE FINDS
A HOME

As a child I feared and resented Papa before I loved him. My earliest recollection of him was a tall man with black curly hair who came home at a certain time on week days and remained home all day on Sundays. I was afraid of him because he always picked me up and tossed me toward the ceiling, catching me as I came down. I was certain that one day he would miss and I'd get hurt. I resented him because when he came home we had to share Mamma with him. She was always there to love us, settle our little quarrels, doctor our bruises, kiss away our tears and no matter what she was doing would stop to listen to anything we had to say.

But the minute Papa came home everything changed. She'd meet him with a kiss. They would hold hands while they talked for a few minutes. She would walk with him to his rocking chair and fuss over him, lighting his pipe or cigar. She'd sit on his lap or the arm of the rocking chair and stroke his hair while they whispered and laughed.

She'd ignore us children while this was going on. I remember I pretended to fall one time and let out a lusty cry of pain. If Papa hadn't been home, Mamma would have taken me in her arms, inspected my bruise and made me well with a kiss. Instead she merely said, "John D., you aren't hurt and you know it. Now be quiet."

In time I learned to tolerate Papa, then enjoy him, and later to love him very much.

We children called two people Aunt and Uncle who weren't related to us. One was Uncle Mark, who was Marshal of West Adenville; the other was Aunt Bertha. She came into our lives the day she walked into the office of *The Advocate,* plunked down her carpetbag and introduced herself in a thick New England accent.

"Name's Bertha Tuttle. The widow Tuttle. You be Tom Fitzgerald, I reckon." As Papa got up from his desk, she continued, "Hail from down Vermont way. Been cooking in the camp boarding house at Castle Rock, nigh on to four years now. Jest buried my husband—that be Mr. Tuttle—t'other day."

Papa shook his head. "I'm sorry to learn of your bereavement, Mrs. Tuttle."

" 'Twas God's will. 'Twere jest a question of time afore God called him. Mr. Tuttle was a consumptive. That's how I brung him out here. Doc Brayton, that be young Doc Brayton, Old Doc died some time ago, 'lowed as how Mr. Tuttle might live a little longer if I brung him out West. I did and I cared fer him. And now the good Lord has called him."

Papa was perplexed. "I'm sorry about your husband's death. Do you want me to print Mr. Tuttle's obituary?"

" 'Twould be right nice of you, but t'aint the reason I'm here. Mr. Tuttle and I aren't blessed with any young 'uns. Now he's passed away, a mining camp ain't a fit place fer a respectable widow. Bertha, I says to myself, find yourself a good family that needs you as much as you need them. Mr. Tuttle used to read that paper of your'n and he'd say, 'Bertha, the man who wrote that editorial is a good man.' So I asks around and found you be a Catholic married to a Mormon. And I says to myself, t'ain't no never mind if a Methodist joins a family like that."

"But—" Papa tried to protest.

"Ain't no other way, Mr. Fitzgerald. Ain't got kith nor kin back East. Can't live alone in a mining camp. Ain't no place for a respectable widow. If it be money, fergit it. It ain't dignified to be a servant. All I be wantin' is a home and be makin' myself useful."

"But my wife might object," Papa said, though he couldn't help smiling.

"Ain't no woman in her right mind objects havin' help around a house, especially when there's four young 'uns. I ain't the imposin' kind, Mr. Fitzgerald, but I already told them to send my trunk from the railway station to your house. I'll stay one month. Then if you or your Missus be of a mind I should leave, there won't be nary an argument."

And that was how Aunt Bertha came to live at our house, where she remained until she died at the age of seventy-nine. During all that time she refused to accept any wages. She would charge material for clothes to Papa's account at the General Store. When she needed cash she'd take it from the extra sugar bowl in the kitchen cabinet and tell Mamma how much she'd taken.

Aunt Bertha was a hulking woman who towered over Mamma. She had big hands and big feet like a man's, soft gray eyes, and big lips from which, strangely for a big woman, came a high pitched voice. She had the first false teeth I'd ever seen and was often misplacing them. Then the whole family would have to hunt until they were found before we could sit down to eat.

The only quarrel Mamma ever had with Aunt Bertha was shortly after the big woman came to live with us. Mamma really laid down the law to Aunt Bertha that day and they were devoted to each other the rest of their lives. To understand the quarrel it is necessary for me to explain my childhood recollections of God and religion. I remember well the Sunday evenings after supper when Papa read from the Bible and Mamma read to us from the Book of Mormon. I remember the singing of the hymns and the fact that I was very partial to the Mormon hymns because to me the louder you sang them, the better they sounded. I remember Papa saying the Rosary and how all of us would then say the Latter-Day Saint version of the Lord's Prayer. I remember the Mormon Primary, where simple Bible stories were read to us and we were taught to make little gifts for our parents. I do not recall a single instance during the years I went to Primary when any Latter-Day Saint religious beliefs or tenets were introduced into the lessons.

To me, Jesus Christ and Christmas were synonymous. The cutting of the tree, the stringing of popcorn and cranberries, the pink stockings Mamma made for us pinned to the tablecloth around our dining-room table, and all the wonder of it. Each year Papa would read to us the story of the Nativity and it always made me cry as I thought of the little Jesus in the manger. Christ to me was all things beautiful, like the snow on the ground, the birds singing in the trees, the petal of a rose, the sunset, the rainbow after a storm.

But God was difficult for me to understand. The God that Papa and Mamma told me about was a friendly, kind, generous God who loved everybody because God was love. God loved all children so much he sent a personal Guardian Angel to watch over each one. When Papa first told me about my Guardian Angel, he pointed at my left shoulder and said, "He is sitting right there on your shoulder, J. D., where he can hear and watch everything you do. He knows everything you think. He will tell you without speaking when you are doing something that will make God cry. He'll report every good thing you do and every bad thing you do to God, who will write it all down in a big book. God sent him to watch over you. He will guard you from harm. And if you are good, when you die, he will show you the way to Heaven."

And even today when I say or do something I know God wouldn't approve, I find myself glancing with anxiety and embarrassment at my left shoulder.

I found my Guardian Angel very tolerant with little boys. He didn't say a word when I gleefully entered into the conspiracy of driving Old Lady Miller crazy. Later, when she became one of our family's dearest friends, I realized that my Guardian Angel had known all along how it would turn out.

The God my parents told me about gave me a warm and cozy feeling deep inside. He was the Father of all the people. When I said or did anything I knew God wouldn't approve, I felt the same way as I did when I said or did anything that would hurt Mamma or Papa. The God I loved was very compassionate and would forgive me if I prayed to Him. I was never afraid of Him. I couldn't understand when I'd hear some kid's mother say to him, "If you do that again, God will punish you." I asked Mamma about this and she told me that God never punished anyone because God was love.

My brother Tom was the cause of the first and only quarrel Mamma and Aunt Bertha ever had. Katie, who was afraid to sleep alone and had always slept with Mamma until Aunt Bertha came, was terribly afraid of harmless little garter snakes. Aunt Bertha caught Tom putting a garter snake in the bed she shared with Katie. She grabbed

Tom by the ear and shouted so loud that Mamma could hear downstairs, "Do you want to burn in everlasting Hell? God will punish you if you ever do the likes of that again."

Mamma rushed upstairs. "Don't you ever dare speak to my children that way. Don't you ever dare to threaten any of my children with God's punishment. I've taught my children to believe that God is love and not some terrible monster that goes around punishing little children."

Tom received three days' silent treatment for punishment. I remember the many times I wished that Papa and Mamma would just give us a good whipping and get it over with instead of the terrible silent treatment. The punishment might last for one day or even a week. During this time neither Papa nor Mamma would speak to us. They would pretend that we didn't exist. Even while we were eating, if we asked one of them to pass something, they pretended they didn't hear.

I remember I was confused about Heaven and Hell until I asked Papa about it. He leaned back in his rocking chair and puffed on his pipe for a moment. "Try to remember the happiest and most joyful moment in your life, J. D. When you go to Heaven, you feel that way all the time. Now, try to remember the unhappiest and saddest moment in your life. That is the way it is in Hades all the time."

I didn't question Papa's description of Heaven and Hell, because when I got a little older, I'd hear people say, "This is heavenly," when they were happy; and they always said, "This is Hell," when they were unhappy or sad.

I remained confused about God even after Aunt Cathie came out West to make us into good Catholics. She began teaching us the Cathechism and told us that God was Three Persons. For a long time, I thought of the Father as being the Father of all the people, and the Son as being the Father of good people like us, and the Holy Ghost as being the God of the people who said he'd punish their children.

I enjoyed the Mormon Primary on Saturday afternoons, until Aunt Cathie arrived. I liked listening to the Bible stories, making things, being with my playmates, and the ice cream, cookies, homemade candy, popcorn balls and other treats they used to serve us. I had lots of fun acting in the plays and taking part in some of the portrayals of Bible stories.

Sweyn was baptized a Mormon when he was eight years of age and had reached the age of reason. Tom was also baptized a Mormon. Katie and I never were baptized as Mormons, because Katie was so terribly afraid of water she got hysterical when they tried to get her down to the creek. As for me, my Aunt Cathie came West before I was eight years old.

15

A SUNDAY DINNER with fewer than five guests was a novelty in our house. In those days we called the meal dinner, and it was eaten at two o'clock sharp in the afternoon. The extra leaves for the big oak dining table would accommodate eighteen people. The children always ate first with Mamma's everyday dishes. After the table was cleared, Mamma would put on her real Irish linen tablecloth with napkins to match; remove the cut-glass tumblers from the dining-room buffet, with the matching water pitcher and bowls; open the china closet and take out her set of Haviland china. Last she'd place a bowl of fruit in the center of the table.

They were a strange mixture of people who sat beneath the chandelier with its multi-colored pieces of glass which used to tinkle when there was a draft in the room.

Mamma never knew and Papa would forget how many people he'd invited during the week to come for Sunday dinner. We children liked it when Henri Dussiere, his wife and their son Pierre came, because Mr. Dussiere would bring his accordion, and he and his wife would sing lilting songs in their native Basque. We could not understand a word but we would laugh and laugh because they sounded so funny. The sheepmen and cattlemen would always ask us children to get out the leather sacks containing our gold pieces. They would have us pile the gold pieces up on the floor with the two-dollar-and-a-half pieces in one pile, the five-dollar pieces in another pile. Then they would say that one pile looked a little low and give each of us a gold piece to place upon it.

Sometimes Papa would bring the Chief of an Indian tribe to the house. Mamma would insist she be warned in advance because the Chiefs thought that because they were invited as guests they could have anything in the house. They would go around and point and grunt and pick up anything that struck their fancy.

Uncle Will, Hal Gentry, Judge Baker, Uncle Mark and sometimes Windy Davis came regularly for Sunday dinner. We would watch out the front window, and when Tom saw Judge Baker coming, he'd shout: "Here comes old cherry nose. If the Indians cut off his nose all he'd have to do would be to stick a cherry on it and nobody would know the difference."

How I loved it when Uncle Mark, Uncle Will, Marshal Gentry and Judge Baker came. That meant we could listen to them talk about the ghost town of Silverlode and all the bad men who had lived there.

One of the tales I remember best was the one about Gabriel.

Papa wasn't a drinking man or a gambling man, and he would take his relaxation in visiting the camp grounds almost every night. Leaving *The Advocate* office, he would turn left on Corry Street, walking by Tanner's Livery Stable, past the blacksmith shop, and turn into the camp ground. Here by the light of torches, the men held wrestling matches, foot races, contests of weight lifting, boxing matches, played horseshoes, told tall stories, swapped guns, saddles, wagons, horses and mules, debated on every conceivable subject, sang around the campfires, and listened to traveling evangelists.

One summer evening, Papa was attracted by the large crowd listening to an evangelist who called himself Gabriel. The evangelist was mounted on a large box flanked by two burning torches. On poles driven into the ground he had draped a backdrop of black cloth, and in the center of the backdrop a silver trumpet was suspended.

Gabriel was a tall thin man with a gaunt face and piercing big black eyes, and was dressed entirely in black from his wide-brimmed pancake hat to his boots. As Papa approached, Gabriel raised his long arms skyward. "Repent, ye sinners before it is too late," he shouted in a resonant voice of doom. "This town is the Devil's own kingdom, contaminated by whores, gamblers and purveyors of alcohol. Repent, ye sinners, before it is too late, for as surely as Nebuchadnezzar was cursed with madness believing himself an animal, so shall your licentiousness be a curse upon you. Repent, ye sinners, and prepare for Judgment Day. Seek ye forgiveness and obey the Commandments of the Lord. Cast out the Devil before it is too late. For I am Gabriel, and I have been sent by the Lord Himself that ye may yet be saved. Yea, and if you do not believe this to be true, wait until the hour of midnight Sunday."

He turned and removed the silver trumpet from the backdrop. Holding it aloft, he shouted: "I tell you I have been sent by the Lord himself to save you. The Lord is merciful, the Lord is just. I have been chosen as His instrument for the resurrection of the dead in yon boot hill, so that they, too, may repent and be saved from Hell. At twelve o'clock midnight, Sunday, I shall resurrect the dead in boot hill. If any man among you fear this resurrection, repent, before it is too late."

Papa walked away before the sermon was concluded. He found himself chuckling at the thought of the dead in boot hill being resurrected, reasoning that the majority of the population of boot hill would be more interested in getting even with the living who put them there, than in repenting.

During the next couple of days Gabriel carried his message of impending doom into every saloon and gambling hall in Silverlode. He spent all Saturday night in the cemetery communing with the dead spirits he would bring to life at the sound of his trumpet at twelve o'clock midnight on Sunday.

The Sunday evening preceding Gabriel's advertised performance was the quietest evening in the town's history. The saloons and gambling halls were filled with people; but all of them seemed to be drinking very little, and if gambling, they played listlessly. Men spoke in hushed whispers and sought out only those they knew to be their true friends.

At a table in the 66 Saloon sat five men who were responsible for more than twenty graves in boot hill. Their drinks stood untouched before them.

Texas Slim summed up their collective thinking when he remarked ruefully: "In a fair and square fight agin human bein's, the five of us here could get all twenty afore they got us. But how can you shoot a ghost?"

Red Barron nodded his head. "'Tain't never been done, killin' a ghost, I mean. Maybe this Gabriel can't do what he says."

Lefty Small made circles on the table with his whiskey

glass. "Mebbe yes, mebbe no. There's one sure way to stop him. Kill him before he can blow his damn horn."

Juan Lopez wiped his mustache with the palm of his hand. "Si, amigos, eet ees thee only way. But, we must be careful. To keel an unarmed man weel breeng zee Marshal. He weel hear zee shot. And me, amigos, I have no weesh to tangle with zee Marshal."

The fifth member of the group, Tad Shaner, leaned forward and spoke in a hushed whisper. "I don't believe he can raise the dead, but we can't take a chance. Juan is right, we can't shoot him. There's only one answer. Juan kills him with his knife, see? We all go to the private poker room in the rear, and we all swear Juan don't leave the room, see."

"Si," Juan Lopez nodded. "Thees I weel do. Eet ees easier to keel wan preacher, than to meet two ghosts whom I keeled weeth knife in zee back."

Just before nine P.M. Juan Lopez slipped out the back window from the private poker room on his errand of assassination. The four men remaining had no more compunction about killing a man than they would have about killing a coyote, and yet, as time passed, beads of sweat formed on their foreheads and they were unable to concentrate on their card game. Finally after waiting for more than an hour, Texas Slim slammed down his cards. "I cain't take any more of this. I'm goin' out there."

Lefty Small stood up. "We'll all go. Juan probably got cold feet and skipped town."

The four climbed out the rear window and made their way to boot hill cemetery without being seen. As they approached it, they could see Gabriel sitting on a tombstone, the trumpet on his knees reflecting the rays of the brilliant moon.

Red Barron grumbled. "If I had a rifle, I could pick him off from here."

Tad Shaner held up his hand. "Quiet now. We'll split up, see? Slim, you and Red go down around the left side there. Lefty, you go along the right side, until you come to where the cemetery runs into the mountainside. When you get set, give three hoot owl calls. Don't shoot, just sneak toward the preacher on your hands and knees. We'll grab him and take him up the canyon out of gunshot sound and kill him, see?"

The others nodded, and Tad Shaner sat down to wait. He heard Lefty give the signal in a few minutes and a little later, he heard the signal from Red and Slim. He began crawling toward the silhouette of the preacher, trying to keep in the shadows of the many wooden tombstones. About halfway he rounded a tombstone and his hand came down on something soft. He took his eyes from Gabriel and stared down into the sightless eyes of Juan Lopez. Lefty jumped to his feet. "Help, help," he shouted, then pulling his gun, shot into the air until the chamber was empty, all the while screaming: "Red, Slim, Lefty, come here."

Gabriel remained unperturbed on his tombstone while the three gunmen raced across the cemetery. They all arrived together. Tad Shaner pointed at the body. "It's Juan and he's dead, see?"

Red Barron nodded. "That's good."

Lefty Small demanded: "What's good about it?"

"Don't you see," Red explained, "the preacher killed him. All we gotta do now is take Juan's body into town and show it to the Marshal. He'll arrest him. Then we can stir up the boys and hang Gabriel."

It was a quarter to eleven when the four gunmen carried Juan's body into the Whitehorse Saloon and laid it on a card table. Marshal Gentry and Judge Baker were among the first to crowd around.

"The preacher killed him, Marshal," Red Barron announced. "Juan went up to the cemetery to see if he couldn't talk that preacher out of blowin' his horn. When he didn't come back in an hour we went lookin' for him and found him dead, just like the preacher left him. Do your duty, Marshal, go arrest Gabriel. We'll hold court right here and hang him before midnight."

Hal Gentry bent over the body and began examining it. Finally he straightened up. "No sign of a gunshot wound or knife wound." He motioned to Doc Tethers, who wasn't too drunk. "What do you make of it, Doc?"

Doc Tethers examined the pupils of the eyes and the horror mirrored in the face. "Heart failure," he said shrugging, then walked back to the bar followed by the big hunchback.

Doc's explanation wasn't accepted by very many people. The look on Juan Lopez' face convinced most of them that the Mexican had been scared to death. And there wasn't any human thing that walked on two feet that could scare Juan. Had the Lord sent an angel of wrath to strike down Juan before he could kill Gabriel? Had Gabriel resurrected the two men Juan had killed by a knife in the back a little ahead of time?

As the news of Juan's death in boot hill was spread from saloon to saloon by Windy Davis, a spontaneous reaction seemed to take place all over town. Each man in Silverlode sat face to face with his conscience. In the Whitehorse Saloon Lefty Small put his hat on the bar and dropped several gold pieces into it. Nobody asked the purpose for the collection; but all seemed to understand. The contributions were in proportion to the fear engendered by the conscience of each man. At first there was a sort of a shamefaced attitude on the part of the contributors, but as the hour of midnight drew near, lines had to be formed to accommodate them.

And through it all, Uncle Will sat at the big poker table in the Whitehorse Saloon offering two-to-one odds that Gabriel wouldn't resurrect a single occupant of the cemetery. He didn't get any takers, because Dandy Allen pointed out that if Uncle Will failed to win his bet, he wouldn't be around to pay off.

At eleven-thirty a delegation consisting of Hal Gentry, Judge Baker, and Texas Slim were chosen to take the collections made in the various saloons and gambling halls to the cemetery and attempt to negotiate with Gabriel. As the three men started for boot hill, the saloons and gambling halls emptied behind them. Miners, muckers, gamblers, freighters, cowboys, trappers, faro dealers, bartenders, saloon keepers, dance hall girls and all the flotsam and jetsam of a mining camp walked toward the cemetery, and from a distance completely surrounded it. They watched as the three chosen men approached Gabriel.

Groans escaped from the crowd as they saw Gabriel shake his head in the bright moonlight after Judge Baker had talked to him. Here and there in the crowd men and dance hall girls fell to their knees and tried to remember long forgotten prayers. As midnight drew closer, more and more followed this example, as they watched Judge Baker talk and Gabriel shake his head. It was one minute to midnight when a great cheer went up from the watchers as they saw Gabriel climb down from his tombstone and start walking out of the cemetery with the delegation.

Gabriel had driven a hard bargain. He'd accepted the eighteen hundred and seventy-eight dollars in gold pieces with the reservation he would use it to take the message

of the Lord to other mining camps. He insisted that Marshal
Gentry, Texas Slim and Judge Baker remain with him in
his room at the Miner's Hotel until the morning stagecoach
left for Salt Lake City, and guarantee him safe conduct there.
He refused to hand over the silver trumpet until he was
aboard the coach the next morning.

After dinner we'd often change back into our everyday
clothes. We'd keep looking at Uncle Will until finally he'd
say, "Marshal Gentry and Marshal Trainor, I believe there's
a band of outlaws headed this way."

Tom, Sweyn and I, our arms loaded with empty bottles
and cans, would lead the parade to the creek. We'd place the
bottles and cans on logs and in the crotches of trees. Then
we'd get behind a log and start screaming. "Thar's Blackie
Dalton sticking his head over that thar log." Uncle Will's
pearl-handled pistol would boom, and the can or bottle representing the outlaw would go flying through the air. "Look
out, Marshal," I'd scream, "Lefty Lammons is hidin' in that
thar tree." Either Uncle Mark or Marshal Gentry would
draw their guns and another outlaw would bite the dust.
We'd remain until all the cans and bottles representing the
outlaw band had been decimated. When we returned,
Mamma would gently scold Uncle Will. He'd smile at her
and say, "I'm sorry, Princess, but that gang of desperadoes
meant to take over the town. We barely stopped them in
time."

Once I asked Uncle Will why he called Mamma Princess.
"Your father," he said, "like any Irishman worth his salt,
claims to be descended from the Kings of Ireland, though

between you and me, John, this is pure blarney. But your mother is descended from the Kings of Denmark who beat the pants off the English, which was something the Irish never did do."

For many years after, I thought that wars were fought by soldiers beating other soldiers with sticks until their pants fell off.

I remember how I couldn't believe the miracle when faucets were put into our sink and the water pump removed. To be able to get water without pumping was a mystery to me. An even greater miracle was the big twelve-foot kitchen range Papa bought, and hooked the water tank to it. To be able to get hot water right out of the tap instead of heating it in the big copper-bottomed wash tubs was unbelievable.

One day I entered the bathroom from the back porch right after Grandma had left it after taking a bath. I'd been playing cowboys and Indians, and when I saw Grandma's wig on the chair, I picked it up and ran into the kitchen screaming, "Poor Grandma, the Indians done scalped her."

Mamma stopped stirring some cake batter and took the wig from me. "John D.," she said firmly, "you must promise me you'll never tell anyone about this."

Grandma came into the kitchen with a towel wrapped around her head. "Grandma Elizabeth," I blurted out in breathless admiration, "were you really scalped by the Indians?"

She laughed and tousled my hair with her fingers. "Let me put it this way, John, I lost all my hair crossing the plains."

I knew she was just being modest. "Can I see the scars, Grandma, please?"

She laughed again. "I'm afraid they are all healed. It was a long, long time ago." She removed the towel and bent over so I could see her bald head, as Mamma said, "Mother, please! How could you?"

I stared in fascination at Grandma's bald head. Finally I summoned the courage to reach out and touch it. "Gee," I said with admiration, "I'll betcha there isn't anybody got a Grandma who's been scalped by the Indians, like me."

"John D.," Mamma said severely, "please refrain from using the word 'betcha.' And, young man, you listen very carefully to what Mamma is going to say. You must promise never to tell anyone that Grandma wears a wig."

I promised, but I broke my word at my next birthday party.

I remember Papa being terribly busy. He was always writing letters and mailing copies of his newspapers free to politicians and people all over with editorials about statehood for Utah. I remember Papa taking us all to Salt Lake City and his holding me up in his arms so I could see Heber M. Wells, the first Governor of Utah. I remember Bishop Aden bringing the telegram to our house on January 4, 1896, saying that President Cleveland had proclaimed Utah as the forty-fifth state of the Union. I remember how Bishop Aden and Papa shook hands, then put their arms around each other and cried like babies. I remember the bonfires, the band playing and marching up and down Main Street, the singing and the dancing in the streets, the fireworks and the hundreds of people going in and out of our house all day.

But I remember the next day even more because it was my birthday. All my playmates came to our house. There were cakes, cookies and ice cream. I opened all my presents.

It was winter time and so we began playing games in the house like Heavy, heavy hangs over my poor head; Button, button whose got the button; Hide the thimble, and other childhood amusements which seemed so much fun then. When we grew tired of playing games, we began what to most of us was the best game of all, bragging about our families and possessions.

I was a little jealous of Frank Davis, who was about a year older than I. The other kids including the girls acted as if he was some kind of a hero. "There ain't a smarter sheep dog than my dog Shep," he said. Nobody could deny it.

I said, "Don't say 'ain't,' Frank. You should say 'isn't.' My Papa is the best educated man in Adenville and has a college diploma to prove it."

But my friends weren't interested in academics. "My Paw," Frank boasted, "is the best sheep shearer in the world."

Harold McKnight spoke up. "My Paw's the best bronco buster in the world."

Eddie Andrews the son of the blacksmith threw out his chest. "My Paw is the strongest man in the world."

The girls entered the bragging contest. Jane Purdy said her mother made the best pies in the world and that was why she won all the blue ribbons at the county fair.

It was my birthday and I felt cheated. I was desperate. I held up my hands for attention. "My Grandma Elizabeth was scalped by Indians," I said defiantly.

I gloried in their open-mouthed astonishment.

Finally Frank Davis challenged me, "You're fibbing, John, and you know it."

"I am not," I shouted back at him. "I saw and felt Grandma's head. She hasn't got a hair on it. She was scalped by the Indians when crossing the plains and I'll prove it next time she visits us."

They all crowded around me. I had become the most envied and popular boy in West Adenville by virtue of Grandma's bald head.

I enjoyed my new-found fame for weeks, but I began to worry about it as the weather got better and I knew Grandma and Grandpa Neilsen would soon be coming to visit us. The skeptics among my friends kept asking my brothers when Grandma and Grandpa Neilsen were coming. They knew almost as soon as I did when the news reached Mamma that my grandparents would arrive the following Saturday.

In desperation, I took my problem to Tom, who consented to devote his great brain to conceiving a plan that would get me off the hook providing I paid his price. The price was high. I had to promise to do all his chores for a month, give him my braided leather whip and fifteen cents in cash.

The day Grandpa and Grandma Neilsen drove into town a dozen kids followed them right up to the gate of our corral. My friends all crowded around me and demanded to know when I'd prove Grandma had been scalped by the Indians. I ran into the barn and hollered up to the loft to Tom. He came down the rope ladder. "Stop worrying, J. D.," he said. "My great brain will save the day for you. Listen carefully."

I was wide-eyed with admiration for my brother's great brain. I am afraid I let my enthusiasm run away with me. I not only challenged the skeptics to be on hand for Grandma's unveiling, but also issued invitations to almost every kid in town. Long before curtain time, kids began lining up along the picket fence across our front yard.

Grandpa and Grandma Neilsen were right on schedule. Since they always came out and sat on our front porch for about an hour before supper time, my brother's great brain had to figure out a way of allaying any suspicions they might have had concerning the large number of kids along the fence. Pete Hanson, who was the best squaw wrestler in town for his age, was on our front lawn. One by one he was challenging all the kids to wrestle him. At the count of one they would raise their right legs, while lying on their backs. At the count of two they would lock legs. At the count of three they would see who could push his opponent's leg down. Pete won every time.

My brother Tom opened the screen on our upstairs window and crept to the edge of our front porch. When he was ready he gave me the signal by whistling like a whippoorwill. The sight of my brother on the roof over our porch and the kids lined up against the fence attracted the attention of several adults.

I walked over and challenged Pete to wrestle. At the count of one we raised our legs, at the count of two we locked them, at the count of three, Pete following instructions put all his strength into the move and sent me tumbling head over heels. I immediately grabbed my leg and began to bawl. "It's broke. My leg is broke."

Grandma Elizabeth was out of the porch swing at the first yelp. As she came running from the porch, my brother Tom on the roof expertly swung a fish line with a hook on it and snatched Grandma's wig right off her head. She was so intent on her supposedly injured grandchild she didn't even know it.

My brother beat a hasty retreat back through the window, out the back window, down a tree and to the barn where he expected to establish a perfect alibi.

All the kids along the fence began screaming, "Look! Look! It's true. She's been scalped by the Indians."

I shivered with fright as I saw Grandpa coming, the wig in his hands. Then I heard Grandma laugh. She'd found there was nothing wrong with me and had seen Grandpa holding the wig. She pulled me to my feet. "I hope, John, that the childhood treasures you charged for this exhibition were worth it."

"But Grandma," I protested, "I didn't charge anything. Honest Injun, I didn't. They wouldn't believe me when I told them you had been scalped by the Indians."

Grandma took the wig from Grandpa. "You boys asked for proof, now you've seen it," she said to the kids lining the fence.

Frank Davis jumped up and down waving his arms and shouting, "Hurrah for Grandma Neilsen!" The rest of the kids took up the cheering.

Grandma bowed to them and said, "Thank you, boys." Swinging the wig by her side she walked back and into the house with the cheers of the audience ringing in her ears. What she said gave me a place in the hall of fame for years to come. I looked at Grandpa, who was now smiling, and placed my hand in his.

"Gosh Grandpa," I said reverently, "I'll betcha I got the most wonderful Grandma in the world."

Grandpa squeezed my hand. "I'll betcha you have, John. At least I have thought so for many, many years."

When Mamma heard about it, she knew that only Tom's great brain could have conceived the plan. But Grandma wouldn't let her punish my brother or me.

For the remainder of my childhood whenever my playmates began to brag about their parents or relatives, I just remained quiet. I knew that sooner or later some kid would say, "Shucks, that ain't nothing. John's Grandma was scalped by real Indians."

I carried my fame with dignity. I'd nod my head and modestly admit that while Grandpa Neilsen was killing twenty Indians, other Indians grabbed Grandma and tied her to the stake. They scalped her before Grandpa could kill twenty-seven more Indians and rescue her.

16

DIRTY DAWSON AND THE
MAGIC BELT

ONE OF THE KEENEST disappointments of my life was the
first time I saw the ghost town of Silverlode. After all the
tall tales I'd heard, I guess I expected it to be as it had been
in the old days instead of deserted. It was much more excit-
ing to go to East Adenville and see the railway roundhouse
or the Indians at the big camp grounds. But we were all forbidden to go to East Adenville unless we had an adult with us.

From the depot which was on our side of the tracks you
could see East Adenville's Main Street, lined with saloons,
hotels, cafes and shops. The biggest building was my Uncle
Will's Whitehorse Saloon.

There weren't many kids in East Adenville. There were
only five who attended the Mormon school with us, but
there were about a half a dozen others whose parents didn't
believe in education or just didn't care.

One hot August afternoon my brother Tom and I went
down to the depot to play train whistles. We'd sit and wait
for the 2:15 freight to whistle before turning the bend and
then guess the number on the engine pulling her. Then
we'd wait for the 3:30 passenger train and do the same.
While we were waiting for the freight train we saw a

brightly painted medicine man's wagon, pulled by a team of white horses with plumes on their heads. An Indian Chief sat beside a man in a high silk hat as the wagon went down East Adenville's Main Street. A sign on the wagon proclaimed that the "World's Greatest Doctor," had arrived in town. His name was Dr. Willoby Hibby, M.D., Ph.D., P.S.D.

The temptation was too much. Without a word to each other my brother and I crossed the tracks and began to follow the wagon. We'd gone only a short distance when a kid pulling a homemade cart filled with empty bottles blocked our way. He was dressed in rags and was the dirtiest kid I'd ever seen. He had reddish hair that hadn't been cut or combed in months. He let go the tongue of his homemade cart and spit on his hands.

"What you Mormon kids doing in my town?" he demanded belligerently.

I was ready to apologize and run. He was as big as my brother Sweyn. But Tom just stood there and said, "Who says you own East Adenville?"

The boy spit on his hands again. "I do. My name's Dirty Dawson. I kin lick any kid in East Adenville and any two Mormon kids. You danged Mormon Dudes oughtta stay where you belong."

In West Adenville there were certain rules of decorum about fighting. You had to knock a chip off a boy's shoulder or cross a line drawn in the dirt. This boy didn't know the rules. He charged us, and the next thing I knew I was sitting on the ground with my nose bleeding. My brother was sitting next to me with a black eye. But he didn't have sense enough to stay down. He got up only to receive a bloody nose.

"Had enuff?" Dirty Dawson sneered as he spit on his hands again.

Tom nodded as he got slowly to his feet. "I'll be back," he said as we started home.

I was blubbering, but Tom told me to shut up. "My great brain will figure out a way to take care of Dirty Dawson."

Mamma was more upset about us crossing the tracks than she was about our bruises. Papa just asked us if we were afraid. Tom said he wasn't, but I had to admit I was. Papa looked at me. "It isn't whether you lose or win that counts, but only whether or not you were afraid to fight."

About two months later, Tom received a package at the post office. He swore me to secrecy as we went up to the loft in the barn to open it. The package contained a belt with metal discs inside it.

"Behold," he cried holding it up, "the miracle of the ages. A magic belt. Wear it one week and have the strength of ten men."

I was doubtful. "What makes you think it will work?"

"It's guaranteed," he said. "It says so right in the advertisement in the magazine. It's guaranteed, or your money will be cheerfully refunded."

A week later all I noticed was that Tom had red marks around his waist where the metal discs pressed against his skin. We cut the grass and did our chores that Saturday morning, then started out for East Adenville. I suggested to my brother it might be good strategy first to test his strength, or take along about six of our playmates.

"J. D.," he said patronizingly, "the belt is guaranteed. It says so right in the magazine. Besides I can feel I'm ten times stronger than I ever was."

We took a roundabout way to East Adenville, and entered it through the alley behind the buildings so we couldn't be seen from the west side of the tracks. Tom found a vacant lot. He cupped his hands to his mouth and shouted, "Come out, Dirty Dawson, wherever you are, you yellow-bellied skunk." He kept yelling his challenge until a kid came and took a look at us. He returned in a short time with Dirty Dawson.

Tom removed his shirt. The belt gleamed in the sunlight. He drew a line in the dirt with the toe of his shoe. "Cross that line, Dirty Dawson, and I'll make you eat dirt."

I became really frightened. In East Adenville we were satisfied to make a kid say he'd had enough. When you fought to make a boy eat dirt you had to win, or suffer the most degrading defeat anybody could.

Dirty Dawson spit on his hands and jumped over the line. Tom waded into him, but Dirty using his longer reach knocked Tom off balance and then dumped him on the ground with an uppercut. Tom bounded up only to be knocked down again immediately.

Several grownups began to gather around, including Windy Davis. When he saw it was Tom fighting he went to get Marshal Gentry. Some man I didn't know spoke up. "The young one is a head shorter. It ain't a fair fight."

A man I found out later was Dirty Dawson's father had joined the crowd. "My boy didn't start this fight. It was t'other way around. Leave 'em be."

I stood there with tears in my eyes as I watched my brother get knocked down time after time, only to get right back up, rub his hands on the magic belt and go in swinging. Dirty wasn't unmarked and a lot of Tom's blows were landing. Dirty was puffing like a steam engine. Then I noticed that Dirty was hitting Tom more often than he was being hit, but he wasn't knocking my brother down any more. Suddenly Tom let go with a haymaker that caught Dirty on the chin and down he went. When he got up, Tom knocked him down again.

Dirty's father rubbed his unshaven chin. "Mebbe we oughta stop 'em 'fore my boy kills that Fitzgerald kid."

I hadn't noticed Marshal Gentry until he spoke. "You were singing a different tune when your boy was winning. Just stand right where you are."

The more tired Dirty got, the stronger Tom seemed to grow. Dirty could hardly hold up his hands; but Tom seemed to be swinging punches as hard as when they started to fight. Tom hit Dirty on the jaw so hard he spun clear around before he fell on his face.

Tom grabbed the collar of Dirty's shirt. "I said I'd make you eat dirt, you yellow-belly. Now eat it."

"I won't," Dirty cried, then appealed to his father. "Paw, make him stop."

Hal Gentry grabbed Dawson's arm and held him.

Tom pulled Dirty to his feet and smacked him right on the nose. As Dirty went down, Tom jumped on top of him. He grabbed Dirty by the hair and pulled his head back. He scooped up a handful of dirt and forced it into Dirty's mouth. Satisfied, he stood up. He looked around at the kids and grownups watching and announced, "My name is T. D. Fitzgerald and I can lick any kid in East Adenville."

Marshall Gentry came over to where I was helping my brother put on his shirt. "You licked him fair and square, Tom," he said. "Now be as big a man as your father and shake hands."

Tom considered for a moment, then walked over to Dirty, who was standing with tears of humiliation running down his cheeks. Tom stuck out his hand. "No hard feelings, Dirty. I just wanted to show you that nobody can push a

Fitzgerald around. If you ever want to come over to my house, I'll show you my loft in the barn."

Dirty shook hands. "Thanks," he said as if bewildered, "but my Paw says I can't go to Mormontown."

"Don't let that stop you," Tom said. "If anybody tries to stop you, you just tell them that T. D. Fitzgerald said you could come."

Dirty Dawson came trudging up the alley in back of our house the very next day. We were dressed in our Sunday clothes, trying not to get dirty as we played Duck-on-a-Rock. Seth Smith saw Dirty first. "Scat," he shouted. "Get back where you belong."

Tom kicked Seth in the pants. "I invited Dirty to come here and anybody that don't like it can leave."

Seth rubbed the seat of his pants. "If you'd rather play with him than me, I'll go." He looked at Froggy Barlow. "Coming, Froggy?"

Froggy shook his head as Dirty held out an odd-shaped green bottle toward Tom. "It's the purtiest bottle I ever found," he said. "I brung it fer you because I want to be your friend."

Tom took the bottle and carefully examined it. He nodded, "It sure is a pretty bottle. Thanks a lot. I'll put it on Chief Obobo's altar. Come with me and I'll show you my loft."

The Altar of Chief Obobo in the loft consisted of an old camp stove with the skull of a coyote, an Indian war bonnet, a bow and arrow, and other Indian relics piled on it. The floor of the loft was covered with an old horse blanket.

There was a big box used as a table and smaller boxes to sit upon. From nails driven into the rafters hung an old lantern, a horse collar and an assortment of all the things grownups throw away and little boys pick up.

We had eaten our Sunday dinner at two o'clock. We would, as usual, eat supper about seven. At four-thirty Mamma called for us to come in for our collation. I went to the barn and hollered up at Tom. I was in the kitchen when he walked in bold as brass with Froggy and Dirty. "Mamma," he said, "I brought my two friends for ice cream and cake. You know Froggy Barlow, and this is Dirty Dawson."

Aunt Bertha threw up her hands. "What next?"

But all Mamma said was, "That's fine, Tom D. Now all of you go into the bathroom and wash up."

When they came back, Dirty's hands were clean, but his face was still very dirty. Mamma pretended she didn't notice. We sat around the big kitchen table. Dirty ate two pieces of cake and drank three glasses of milk besides putting away a big dish of ice cream.

After we'd finished, Mamma looked at Dirty's face. His eye was black and he had cuts and bruises all over it from the fight. "What is your name, young man?" Mamma asked.

Dirty swallowed hard and hung his head. "Earnest, but everybody calls me Dirty."

Mamma leaned over and looked at his face. "I'm afraid you might get an infection, Earnest," she said. "Come into the bathroom with me and I'll fix up your face." Mamma washed Dirty's face, bathed his black eyes with boric acid solution, washed out the bruises with peroxide and put healing salve on the cuts. She brought him back into the kitchen. She looked at him for a moment, then said, "Earnest, I want you to know you are welcome in this house any time. Ask your father if you can come to dinner next Sunday."

Dirty backed away from Mamma. His mouth was moving but no words came out. His eyes filled with tears. He turned and ran out of the kitchen.

Mamma shook her head sadly. "Poor little fellow." Then she turned to Tom. "I want you to be that boy's friend, Tom D. I want you to be kind to him and treat him exactly as you do your other friends."

Aunt Bertha protested. "Tena, you know who that boy is. He isn't fit company for decent children."

Mamma put her hands on her hips, meaning she was angry. "I do not believe like father, like son. One of God's blessings is the granting to each person born the dignity of being an individual. I know there is good in that boy. I know because he cried when I was kind to him. A bad boy would have been sullen. And, Bertha, I'm perfectly capable of helping my children choose their playmates."

Marshal Gentry had told Papa about the fight. When Papa came home that evening he asked my brother to remove the belt. He looked at it and handed it back. "It is sheer humbug," he said. "As for your being able to beat the Dawson boy, there is a logical explanation for it. You believed so much in the belt that your mind took control of your muscles. That is why you didn't get tired. Now put the belt back on, T. D., and we'll go out to the woodshed where I'll prove to you that the belt is humbug."

Papa made Tom try to lift a heavy log. My brother could lift only one end of it with the belt on. Papa made Tom take the belt off and try again. Tom could still lift only one end of the log. The magic belt joined the other items on Chief Obobo's altar.

A few days later I noticed that Tom began to disappear every day. I was curious and once I followed him to East Adenville, where he met Dirty. They went all over town picking up empty bottles and putting them in Dirty's cart. Then they went to the rear of the Allies Saloon and knocked on the door. A man in a white apron came out, counted the bottles and gave Dirty some money. They spied me when they came back into the street.

Tom made me swear I wouldn't tell Papa or Mamma. "You see, J. D., Dirty has to collect empty bottles to get enough money to buy his father whiskey and food. When he does it alone, it takes all day. When I help him we get through in half a day and Dirty can come over to our place and play."

I didn't tell Mamma or Papa, but somebody did. That night Papa was very quiet at supper. He waited until we'd eaten and were sitting in the parlor.

"I know about your helping the Dawson boy collect bottles and selling them to the saloon keepers in East Adenville, T. D. I'm not going to punish you for it because helping another is a fine thing to do. But you must realize that your mother and I have certain social obligations to the community. I forbid you to do it again."

"But, Papa, then Dirty won't ever get a chance to play."

Papa nodded. "I've made an arrangement with your Uncle Will. You tell the Dawson boy just to take all the bottles he has collected by noon of each day to the back door of the Whitehorse Saloon. Your Uncle Will or Jim the bartender will give him enough money to take care of himself and his father. When school begins, I will arrange with your

Uncle Will to see that the boy's father has enough whiskey for his sickness and food for himself and the boy."

"Thanks, Papa," Tom said. Then very seriously, he asked: "What kind of sickness has Dirty's father got that he needs whiskey all the time?"

Papa leaned back in his rocking chair. "It's a sickness of the mind, T. D., and sometimes, as in the case of Mr. Dawson, there is no cure for it."

When our new suits arrived from the mail order house a few weeks before school started, there was an extra one for Dirty Dawson. Mamma had Tom bring Dirty to supper the day before school started. She made Dirty take a bath and then got him all dressed up in his new suit. He certainly looked different and even Katie, who had stuck up her nose at him, was impressed.

If any of us children had eaten the way Dirty ate Mamma would have raised cain. He picked up his food in his fingers and crammed it into his mouth; he made loud smacking noises and didn't keep his lips closed when chewing. Mamma had never tried to correct his manners during the several meals he'd eaten at our house until that evening.

"Enjoy your supper, Earnest," she said, "but you should learn to eat more slowly. If you don't, when you grow older you will have ulcers and be sickly."

It must have been the first time that Dirty was conscious of how he ate. His eyes filled with tears. He brushed them away with his sleeve, and looked across the table at Tom. For the first time he picked up a knife and fork. He kept his eyes glued on Tom and imitated him. Tom would take a forkful of food and put it in his mouth; Dirty would do the same. All through the meal Dirty ate the exact number of mouthfuls as Tom.

When it was time for Dirty to go home, Mamma kissed

him on the cheek. Poor Dirty began to blubber like a calf and ran out of the parlor.

We waited the next morning in front of school until the teacher rang the bell, but Dirty didn't show up. The first day of school lasted only a half a day. We ran all the way home to tell Mamma that Dirty hadn't been to school.

Mamma's chin seemed to jut out a little defiantly as she listened. She went into her bedroom. When she came out she was wearing her velvet hat with plumes, her long black gloves that reached to her elbows, her cameo pin fastened to her pleated blouse, and her best tailored suit. She told Aunt Bertha to give us our lunch.

Sweyn, Tom and I decided to forego lunch to follow Mamma. Without looking to right or left she went right down Main Street and marched across the tracks into East Adenville. Paying no attention to the loungers in front of the saloons who ogled her, she turned into the alley where Tom had said Dirty lived with his father. She went right up to the door of the shack and knocked. When she received no answer, she called: "Open your door this instant, Mister Dawson. I know you're in there. This is Mrs. Fitzgerald. Open this door, do you hear me?"

Sweyn looked scared. "What if he's drunk and hurts Mamma?"

Tom nodded. "I'll go get Uncle Will."

Dirty's father swung open the door of the shack. His hair was mussed and he hadn't shaved. His eyes were bleary and his clothes looked as if he'd slept in them. He was very thin, but his face had what Papa called the "whiskey bloat."

"Produce your son, Mr. Dawson," Mamma commanded.

"Now look here," Mr. Dawson said angrily, "don't get uppity with me, Mrs. Fitzgerald. I know my rights. He's my kid and I don't need no meddlin' female to tell me how to raise him. Tryin' to make a Dude outa him so he'll be ashamed of his Paw. Puttin' high-falutin' idears in his head 'bout keepin' clean, gittin' learnin', wearin' fancy clothes. You leave my young-un be, you meddlin' female. You hear me? You leave my young-un be."

"Now you listen to me," Mamma said shaking her finger at him. "You forfeited every right you had as a father when you tried to drag that fine sensitive boy down to your own level. You ought to be horsewhipped for making that poor child live with you in this stinking, degrading and foul environment."

"Ah shut up," Dawson interrupted, "you and your high-falutin' words."

"I certainly will not shut up," Mamma said, "if the men in this town haven't the civic sense of duty to tell you a few truths about yourself, then I will. I do not care a fig what you do with yourself. But I will not stand idly by and permit you to ruin that boy's life. Now produce your son, this minute, do you hear me. This minute."

Dirty appeared in the doorway beside his father. His face was all swollen and the new suit torn to shreds. "Please go away, Mrs. Fitzgerald," he pleaded, "Paw ain't feelin' so good today."

Dawson gave his son a whack on the side of the head that sent Dirty sprawling inside the shack.

Mamma shook her finger at Dawson. "You horrible, brutal beast," she cried.

Dawson got a peculiar look on his face. "Mebbe you need some of the same, you meddlin' female. Now git back across the tracks where you belong and leave us be before I lose my temper."

"You don't scare me, you miserable coward," Mamma defied him.

I saw Dawson lurch from the doorway toward her and screamed, just as Uncle Will arrived with Tom. Uncle Will surprised me by speaking sharply to Mamma. "Go home, Princess, and leave everything to me."

Mamma shook her head. "I will not budge one inch unless Earnest goes with me."

Dawson turned to Uncle Will. "Get this damn meddlin' female out of here."

The words were scarcely out of his mouth when Uncle Will's fist connected with it, knocking Dawson to the ground. Uncle Will pulled the man to his feet and jammed the barrel of one of his pearl-handled guns in Dawson's belly. "I'll blow a hole in you right here and now if you dare swear in front of the Princess again."

Dawson rubbed his hand over his bleeding mouth. His eyes filled with fright. "Didn't mean no harm to the lady, Will. Honest I didn't. Jest don't want no meddlin' female fillin' my boy with high-falutin' idears. 'Tain't right to take a kid from his Paw."

Mamma spoke up. "No one is attempting to take your son away from you, Mr. Dawson. I just want him to have the same opportunity as other boys. I just want him to be able to go to school and have at least one full meal a day at my house. He can come home to you every night as long as you don't abuse him and if you'll clean this place up. I have some old furniture I can give you."

Dawson turned to Uncle Will. "But I need the boy, Will. I'm a sick man. I can't work. I need the boy."

Uncle Will sneered. "You are only as sick as the whiskey you drink makes you. But if that's all that is worrying you, I'll make you a proposition. Let the boy go to school. Let him eat one meal a day at Mrs. Fitzgerald's. Stop beating the boy. Clean this place up. You agree to this and I'll see

you get all you want to drink at the Whitehorse. I'll arrange
for your meals at the Frontier Cafe. The first time you try
to stop the boy from going to school or beat him, I'll fix
it so no saloon keeper in this town will give you a drink
even if you can pay for it. Is it a deal?"

Dawson was smiling as he nodded his head.

Dirty didn't know beans about school. He had to sit in
the front row with all the little kids. Tom's great brain
helped Dirty a lot. Tom taught Dirty how to add and sub-
tract by putting marbles on the ground and moving them
from one pile to another. He taught Dirty how to divide by
cutting up apples. He taught him the alphabet and phonics
like B for bottle, C for candy. Papa gave Dirty lessons in
penmanship. Mamma spent hours with Dirty over his school
books. With all their help Dirty managed to jump two
grades his first year in school.

When Dirty learned to write, Mamma said he wrote a
beautiful hand that showed artistic talent. She taught him
how to draw with crayons and paint with water colors. Some
of his drawings and paintings didn't look very good to me,
but Mamma always praised them.

Uncle Will was indirectly responsible for the death of Mr.
Dawson. Dirty's father expired in his shack one night from
the effects of acute alcoholism about seven months after he'd
made the bargain with Uncle Will. Dirty discovered his
father dead when he got up that morning to go to school.
He hurried to school and told my brother Tom about it.
Tom felt that nobody would miss Mr. Dawson until after
school, and so he would have a chance to put his great brain
to work on the problem.

When school was over they went to the shack. Tom held
a mirror in front of Mr. Dawson's mouth and solemnly pro-

nounced him dead. It wasn't until then that Dirty broke down crying.

Tom shook his head. "Now he's dead, I'm afraid they'll send you to one of those orphans' homes. I need time for my great brain to figure a plan to save you from the orphans' home. Let's hide enough stuff under our coats to make it look like you ran away. We'll go to the loft and you can hide there until I figure out how to save you."

The next day when Dirty didn't come home for lunch with us, Mamma asked Papa to go to the shack to make certain the boy was all right. Papa found Mr. Dawson dead. A search was instigated for Dirty, but nobody found him. Uncle Will, Papa, Marshal Gentry, Dandy Allen, Windy Davis and Uncle Mark were pallbearers at the funeral. Mamma was the only woman who attended the burial service.

After the funeral Mamma carried on something fierce. "That poor boy," she cried to Papa. "He found his father dead and was afraid he would be sent to an orphanage, so he ran away. You must find him."

Papa had a long talk with Uncle Mark and Marshal Gentry the next day. When he came home he kept looking at Tom all through supper. Later in our parlor he said, "Come here, T. D."

After Tom had walked over, and stood in front of Papa with his hand on Papa's knee, Papa said, "You are taking the Dawson boy's disappearance very lightly, T. D. Now tell me where he is."

Tom wouldn't lie to Papa. He just shook his head. "I won't tell, Papa. They'll put Dirty in an orphanage and he'll die there."

Mamma, who had been behind the beaded curtains separating the parlor from the dining room, had overheard. She entered the parlor and looked at Tom. "You are right, son. Earnest cannot be sent to an orphanage. He needs a home and love. If you know where he is, tell him that I promise I will never let them put him in an orphanage. He can live right here with us."

Papa seemed surprised. "Do you think that wise, Tena girl?"

Mamma stood very straight. "Earnest is a good boy. He has talent that must be developed. He needs a family who love him. Tom D., go get him and bring him here. And children," she looked at us all, "I never want you to call him Dirty again. You must call him Earnest or Earnie."

And that was how Earnie came to live with us. I can't remember a single time when Mamma or Papa treated him any differently from the rest of us children. He received the same love and attention we did. He also received the same silent treatment we did as punishment.

Tom and Earnie had moved all of Earnie's pretty bottles from the shack to our barn. I remember the day I heard the sound of breaking glass and entered the barn. Earnie was breaking all his bottles. He had tears in his eyes. When I asked him the reason, he told me he was going to make a birthday present for Mamma.

It was some sacrifice. It would have been the same if I'd broken all my genuine Indian arrowheads. I watched as Earnie separated all the different colors of broken glass. He then took a piece of six-inch stove pipe about two feet long and put a wooden plug in one end. I went along with him to the creek where he searched until he found just the right kind of red clay he wanted. We returned to the barn where he mixed the clay with water and then covered the outside of the stove pipe with it. When the clay had almost set, he carefully selected different sizes and colors of the broken glass and stuck them on the clay. It took a long time, but when he'd finished I had to admit the thing was beautiful.

"It sure is pretty, Earnie," I said, "but what is it?"

"It'll be a lot prettier after the clay dries and I shine the pieces of glass," he said proudly.

"But what is it?" I persisted.

He looked as if I'd hurt his feelings. "It's an umbrella stand."

"Oh," I said, "that's what it is. Yes sir, it sure is."

We always gave our birthday presents right after dinner. That year I gave Mamma a beautiful comb that Aunt Bertha had helped me pick out at the store. Papa gave her some earrings. Katie, Tom and Sweyn put their money together and gave Mamma a pair of gloves.

I felt sorry for Earnie when he came into the parlor carrying his crazy umbrella stand, but not for long. Mamma hugged him and kissed him. She raved about how beautiful the stand was. She insisted on putting it in the hallway and getting some umbrellas from a closet and standing them in it. I thought Earnie would burst with pride when Mamma said, "I want you all to know why I consider Earnie's present the best of all. He sacrificed his beautiful bottles to make the present. I shall treasure it forever."

Over the years the furniture in our home changed, but the umbrella stand stayed on. I remember the many times I saw Mamma replacing a piece of glass with clay and how her eyes would grow misty as she did it.

Earnie's first birthday in our house was a special occasion. Mamma gave Earnie as big a party as she ever gave for any of her own children. There were games, prizes, ice cream and cake. Earnie strutted around in his new suit, but every time he looked at Mamma, his eyes would dim with tears. The best part of all came after supper that night.

We children all had silver napkin rings with our initials on them. Earnie just had a plain one. No mention was made of the extra surprise until just before dessert. Mamma reached over and patted Earnie's hand. "We have wanted to adopt you, Earnest, but we found a diary in the shack after your father died. After reading it we knew you would want to keep your father's name. It told of how your father and mother came West and worked in a trading post where you were born. One day when your father was away from the post it was attacked by Indians. Your mother hid you in an empty pickle barrel. But she and the others at the post were all killed. When your father returned, he was so stricken with grief that he got the sickness which made him drink. I tell you this so you will never be ashamed of your parents."

Mamma turned to Papa, who took a box from his pocket and set it on the table. Papa spoke to Earnie. "We want you to keep and always be proud of the name of Dawson, but we would also consider it an honor if you'd take the middle name of Dennis like all the other Fitzgerald men-folk." Papa opened the box and removed a silver napkin ring. "This has the initials E. D. D. engraved upon it." He handed the napkin ring to Earnie.

E. D. Dawson looked at the ring as if it were some kind of precious jewel. He laughed, then cried as he pointed to the initials on it.

Tom got up and ran around the table. "Congratulations E. D.," he shouted. Of course, Sweyn, Katie and I had to do the same thing. Amidst all this Mamma came in carrying a special birthday cake. Tom pointed at the icing on it and shouted, "It says 'Happy Birthday to E. D.'"

Earnie blew out the candles. He laughed. He wept. And we all laughed and wept with him.

17

AUNT CATHIE TO THE RESCUE

DURING HIS HONEYMOON in Denver, Papa had written to his sisters and brother in Pennsylvania that he'd married a Mormon. Being a priest, Uncle John could not voice an opinion. Aunt Cathie and Aunt Josie did not write to Papa for more than a decade.

Papa never talked much about his relatives back East. When the letter arrived with the Pennsylvania postmark on it, Mr. Olsen, the postmaster, brought the letter to our house because Papa wasn't at *The Advocate*. Mamma sent Sweyn to look for Papa while she gave Mr. Olsen some pie and a glass of milk.

Katie was playing jump rope in front of our house when Mr. Olsen arrived. For once in her life she did the right thing and ran to the barn where Tom, Earnie and I were playing. Sweyn found Papa at the L. D. S. Tabernacle discussing some printing with Bishop Aden. Papa hurried home, because he knew that Mr. Olsen delivered in person only very important letters. How Mr. Olsen could tell which letters were important and which ones weren't, nobody knew. Mr. Olsen always remained to find out what the important news was so that he could tell everybody who called at the post office.

We were all waiting in the parlor when Papa arrived with Sweyn. Papa's face seemed to light up with joy when he saw the postmark on the letter. He sat down in his rocker and opened the letter, and we watched his face change from an expression of joy to one of anger, then break into a broad grin as he finished. He threw back his head and roared with laughter. "It's the funniest thing I ever heard," he shouted.

Mamma put her hands on her hips. "You might let Mr. Olsen, who is waiting, and the children and me know what is so funny."

Papa slapped his knee. "It's my sister Cathie. She is coming here. Tena girl, you will be delighted to know that my sister Cathie firmly believes that you and all our children have horns."

Mamma took the letter and read it. We watched for her to break out laughing when she'd finished reading it, but she didn't. Tom bent his head down and pointing his fingers, began running around the room, shouting: "I got horns. I got horns like a steer." Katie, Sweyn and I joined him. Earnie walked over to Mamma and put his arm around her waist.

Mamma said: "I don't think it very amusing. Somehow, I wish your sister had let well enough alone. I resent her implication that she is coming here to make Christians out of us as if we were savages." She turned to us children. "Go outside and play, children. I want to speak to your father alone. And good day, Mr. Olsen."

The postmaster looked at Mamma. "Do you mind if I tell people, Sister Tena. It is just too rich to keep."

Mamma shook her head as we children went outside. Katie invented a game we all liked. She'd draw herself up in a haughty pose and say, "I'm your Aunt Cathie and I came out West to cut off your horns." We'd run with her chasing us as we begged her to spare our horns.

We might have been more charitable of Aunt Cathie if we could have read the letter Aunt Josie wrote to Papa which he received a few days later. It read in part:

My dear brother Tom:

Father John and myself have done our utmost to dissuade Cathie from going West. You would not know, but our dear sister has not been the same since the day her fiancé was instantly killed when the team bringing him to church for his marriage to Cathie ran away. The surrey was turned over, pinning him beneath it and breaking his neck. Cathie turned to religion for solace. Father John and I tried in vain to get her to enter a convent but for some inexplicable reason she refused. As the years passed she gave all her time to the church and spent her inheritance on charity.

As for myself, dear brother, time has somewhat mellowed my biases and I feel ashamed for not having written you. Unfortunately, time has only increased Cathie's religious prejudice to the extent it has become an obsession. I am afraid, dear brother, that Cathie's coming will be a cross to bear. I beseech you to be gentle and kind toward her.

When Cathie advised me that her inheritance was all gone, I offered to take her into my home, to which my husband readily consented. I thought the matter entirely settled until she suddenly told me that she was needed more out West. She told me that God had shown her the way. She must go to you to see that your children are brought up in the Catholic faith and she must bring brother Will back into the Mother Church. There were no arguments that could dissuade her. Father O'Leary and I weren't even able to convince her that Mormons don't have horns.

Please be patient with our dear sister. We all very much fear a mental collapse.

We children knew nothing of this letter until many years later. We did know that Aunt Cathie's coming had made Mamma unhappy. We were playing in the upstairs hallway because it was raining outdoors. Earnie went downstairs to get a drink of water, and when he came back he spoke to Tom. "Missus Fitzgerald is crying in her bedroom and Bertha can't make her stop. Can't your great brain figure out some way to stop your Aunt Cathie from coming here?" Earnie always called Mamma, Mrs. Fitzgerald; and Papa, Mr. Fitzgerald.

Tom got up from the floor with a determined look on his face. "I'm going into the bedroom to put my great brain to work. Please be quiet out here."

Papa and Mamma decided that just he and Uncle Will would meet the train the afternoon Aunt Cathie was due to arrive. Mamma seemed very nervous and upset after they had left. We were all sitting on our big front porch dressed in our Sunday clothes. Tom had instructed us that when we heard the train whistle at the bend to do as he did. Right on time the whistle blew. Tom said, "I'm going to get a drink of water." With cries of "Me too," Sweyn, Earnie, Katie and I followed him into the house.

"Remember, children," Mamma called after us, "I want each of you to kiss your Aunt Cathie and wish her welcome."

We shouted a promise. We waited in the kitchen while Tom went upstairs and returned with a gunny sack filled with steer horns that had recently graced hatracks in many homes. Some of his friends' parents were going to be angry when they got the horns back because Tom had drilled holes in them and fastened elastic bands on them. He showed us each how to put the horn in the center of our foreheads with the elastic band going back over our ears. After Tom had inspected all of us, he said, "We'll wait in the parlor until she enters our gate and starts up the walk toward the porch."

We had a hard time smothering our laughter until Tom warned us it was the only way to make Mamma happy again. The neighbors all up and down the street were watching as Papa pulled the team to a halt in front of our place. While Papa tied the horses to the hitching post, Uncle Will helped a woman, dressed in a travel duster and a big hat tied with a scarf, down from the buggy. Uncle Will opened the gate and Mamma called to us, "Children, your Aunt Cathie has arrived."

With Tom in the lead shouting, "Welcome, Aunt Cathie," the five of us with horns sticking out of our foreheads burst through the front door.

Aunt Cathie took one look at us, let out a piercing shriek and fainted. Uncle Will caught her just in time. Papa and Uncle Will were laughing like crazy. But Mamma was furious as she rushed from the porch. "Take the poor dear and put her in my bedroom," she ordered.

It was the first time a mass punishment was meted out in our home. We were all given the silent treatment for a week. The punishment would have been worth it if the plan had worked, but it didn't.

18

AUNT CATHIE was beautiful in the way a lake in wintertime is beautiful. Her eyes were blue, but never filled with laughter like Mamma's. Her mouth was small and dainty; but she never smiled like Mamma. Her skin was as white as the petals of sego lilies, but there wasn't any of Mamma's color in her cheeks. Her long coal-black hair worn in two long braids around her head like a coronet wasn't as pretty as Mamma's golden hair.

My first impression of Aunt Cathie was that she believed everything was a sin. It was a sin to laugh, a sin to play, a sin to fish, a sin to hunt—everything anybody did was a sin.

Papa used to let us see calves being born. When Aunt Cathie heard about it she told Papa that such sinful sights weren't for the eyes of children. I couldn't understand what she meant. The little baby calf wouldn't have been born if God hadn't wanted it to be born, so how could it be a sin? We always sat up with any bitch we had when her puppies were due. Even Tom with his great brain couldn't figure out why it was sinful for a cow to have a calf.

When Aunt Cathie's trunks arrived, there was one that was filled with crucifixes and statues of the Virgin Mary, the

Christ Child and Saints. She placed a crucifix over every bed in the house including Aunt Bertha's, and she gave each of us children a white porcelain-backed prayer book with small gold hinges and clasps.

Every night after supper we had to study the Catechism for an hour with Aunt Cathie. Tom with his great brain could have mastered the entire Catechism in one reading if he'd wanted; instead, he just tried to make it as hard as possible for Aunt Cathie. One time when she asked him to name the Blessed Trinity, he answered, "The Angel Moroni, Joseph Smith and Brigham Young." Papa overheard him and burst out laughing which was perhaps the reason Aunt Cathie failed to get him to punish Tom.

Another time she said to him: "Now, Thomas, I know you've studied your lesson and know the right answer. Tell me why God is not one but three." Tom knew the answer to be The Father, The Son and The Holy Ghost; but with a perfectly straight face he answered, "There's the Mormon God who is love and sort of a jolly fellow. Then there's the Methodist God who just kind of sits on the side and watches the Mormon God and the Catholic God. Then there's the Catholic God who gets angry when a cow has a calf because it's a sin." This time Tom did get punished; he received the silent treatment for three days.

Grandpa and Grandma Neilsen visited us only once after Aunt Cathie came. All through supper Aunt Cathie had talked and talked. Later, in the parlor, she said it was perhaps too late to convert Grandpa and Grandma to the Mother Church; but they could be thankful she'd arrived in time to prevent their grandchildren from embracing a sinful and pagan religion.

Grandpa was sitting in Papa's rocking chair with his hands resting on his umbrella. He raised the umbrella and pointed it toward Aunt Cathie who was sitting on the sofa. "Listen, woman," Grandpa shouted, "I shudder to think of my grandchildren growing up to become as bigoted, narrow-minded, intolerant and unchristian as you. I heard you during supper accuse me and my good wife of being immoral because we belong to a faith that condones polygamy. I do not subscribe to your belief that men should confess their sins to another man, but I do not ridicule or damn your belief. I refuse to hear any more of your insults. Unlike you, I do believe, as Jesus Christ believed, in compassion, understanding and tolerance; so I apologize for my anger, and I am sincere when I say that I pity you. Yes, I pity you. And now despite the lateness of the hour, I shall hitch up my team and drive back to Enoch with my wife. I shall return to this house only when you have somehow found the true understanding and meaning of the teachings of Jesus Christ."

Papa and Mamma tried in vain to patch things up; but Grandpa made good on his threat and left our house that night.

There was one thing we all liked about Aunt Cathie. When she had anything to say, she said it, and it didn't make any difference if what she said wasn't for the ears of children. The day she found out about Earnie's father, I had a cold and was in bed upstairs. Aunt Cathie came in the side door of the hallway and marched into the kitchen. I could hear her all the way upstairs.

"Tena, I heard it on good authority that this boy Earnest Dawson you have living here was the son of a drunkard and wastrel, and his mother probably a sinful woman. You must remove this evil influence from my brother's children. He will lead them astray Blood will out. He must be sent to an orphanage."

That was the day Aunt Cathie found out she could push Mamma just so far. "Now let you and me understand each other, Cathie," Mamma said, and her voice sounded strange. "Earnest is a good boy. His father may have been a drunkard but only because grief over the killing of his wife by Indians made him so. Earnest will remain in this house for as long as he chooses. If I ever hear you say a single word to him that might hurt his pride or feelings, you'll have to account to me."

"We shall see, Tena," Aunt Cathie answered. "I'll take this matter up with my brother."

"By all means do just that. This is my home and I would no more think of turning Earnest out of it than I would one of my own children."

That evening Mamma said that one hour of studying the Catechism was too much in addition to our school homework. The time was cut to fifteen minutes without Aunt Cathie protesting.

When Aunt Cathie discovered a small Catholic church had been built in Castle Rock she said to Papa, "It seems to me, Thomas, you could have put yourself out to the extent of driving a few miles every Sunday for the salvation of your children's souls."

Papa put down the newspaper he was reading. "And it seems to me, Cathie, that God in His infinite wisdom would know that making children ride twenty-two miles every Sunday would be asking just a little too much, especially during school months when all children look forward to week ends."

I was eight years old when I made my first Holy Communion. We set out for Castle Rock one Saturday morning so we could go to Confession. Mamma didn't go with us, but she prepared three shoe boxes filled with fried chicken, hard boiled eggs, sandwiches, cookies and cake.

Castle Rock was a big disappointment to me. The buildings, the vegetation, even the people, all seemed to be covered with coal dust. Everything looked dirty except the inside of the church. On one side of the altar was a life-sized statue of the Blessed Virgin and Child. On the opposite side was a statue of the patron saint of the church, St. Joseph. I was frightened when I entered the confessional, but under Father Caffarella's guidance I got along fine. After Confession I felt wonderful as if everything was good. I fell asleep on the ride back to West Adenville. Mamma and Aunt Bertha had a big supper waiting for us because we couldn't eat anything from midnight until after Holy Communion the next morning.

At five o'clock in the morning we got up and got dressed in our new clothes. Katie had a white dress Mamma made for her and she looked like an angel in it with her long white lace veil. Sweyn had already made his first Holy Communion. Aunt Cathie wanted Tom, Earnie, Katie and me to make ours together.

During the drive to Castle Rock I wasn't aware of my own thirst and hunger until Tom started complaining. Aunt Cathie kept shushing him, but he just kept on complaining that he was slowly and surely dying of thirst and hunger. Remembering how they always gave us ice cream and cake at the Mormon Primary, Tom finally blurted out, "I know now what the difference is between the Mormons and the Catholics."

"And what is that, Thomas?" Aunt Cathie asked, no doubt expecting Tom to speak of the advantages of Catholicism.

"The Mormons feed you and the Catholics starve you,"

my brother replied. Papa laughed, but Aunt Cathie was quite angry.

My first Holy Communion seemed the most wonderful and inspiring thing that ever happened to me. The pageantry, the glory, the sacredness of the Mass and Communion brought me extreme ecstasy. My childish mind kept comparing the austerity of the Mormon services with the pomp and ceremony of the Catholic Mass. I cried when it was all over.

Papa treated us to a surprise by taking us all to the town's only restaurant for breakfast. On the way back home, Sweyn, Katie, Earnie and I kept talking about how beautiful and wonderful the Mass and Communion had been. Tom just sat staring at the road.

Mamma had a big chicken dinner waiting for us when we returned. After eating, we had to take a nap because of the early hour we'd got up. When we woke up we went out to play until supper time, except Tom, who sat in the parlor reading his almanac.

Mamma and Aunt Bertha washed the supper dishes. Aunt Cathie never helped with any of the dishes or housework. When Mamma and Aunt Bertha came into the parlor, Tom walked over to Mamma.

"Mamma," he said looking up at her, "let's sing some hymns like we used to on Sunday nights before Aunt Cathie came."

Aunt Cathie spoke up quickly. "You're a Catholic now, Junior, and soon you will learn how to sing Catholic hymns in Latin as well as English."

Tom ignored her. "Please Mamma, let's sing 'Come, Come Ye Saints.' "

"Your Aunt Cathie was speaking to you, Tom D.," Mamma said.

Tom shrugged. "You must be mistaken, Mamma. My

name isn't Junior. And she's got no right to tell me what to do and what not to do. She isn't my Mamma. I don't like her and I wish she'd go back where she came from and leave us alone."

Aunt Cathie got up and marched across the room. "If you can't teach your children manners, Tena," she said sharply, "I will." She grabbed Tom by the ear and spun him around. It was a silly thing to do because Tom drew back his foot and kicked her on the shins.

Aunt Cathie let out a shriek. She pointed at Tom. "This is the Godless one. This is the lost one of this generation. Just like Uncle Sean and brother Will. I demand that you punish him, Thomas."

Before Papa could answer, Mamma spoke up. "Cathie, if you ever lay a hand on any of my children or Earnest again, you'll have to leave my house. That the boy kicked you was wrong, but you provoked him into it. I have consented to your supervising the spiritual upbringing of my children, but I, and I alone, shall supervise their moral and physical upbringing."

Papa seemed to grow suddenly very old and weary. Finally he spoke, "Tena is right, Cathie." Then he motioned to Tom. "Come here, T. D."

Tom squared his shoulders and walked over to Papa. "There is something that you and you alone can decide, T. D.," Papa said. "Your mother and I agreed that we would let each child choose his or her own religion. You are old enough to think for yourself. Think hard, T. D. Would you rather not become a Catholic?"

"That's insane," Aunt Cathie shouted, "allowing a mere boy to make a decision like that."

Papa looked sternly at Aunt Cathie. "Be quiet, please," he said. Then he looked at Tom.

Tom didn't flinch. "I want to be a Mormon like Mamma and all my friends," he said.

"Would you mind telling me why, T. D.?" Papa asked.

Tom didn't hesitate. "There's a lot of reasons, Papa. If being a Catholic makes people like Aunt Cathie, I don't want to be like her. I don't like not being able to understand what the priest is saying. In the Latter-Day Saints church I can understand everything Bishop Aden says. I don't like the Catholic God as much as I do the Mormon God."

"But T. D.," Papa protested, "there is only one God."

Tom shook his head. "The Mormon God doesn't get angry at people who laugh and have fun, but Aunt Cathie's God gets mad if you even smile." He stepped back and pointed his finger at Aunt Cathie. "Before she came here we were happy. Even Aunt Bertha was happy, and she's a Methodist. We read the Bible and the Book of Mormon on Sundays. We sang all kinds of hymns and nobody said you could only sing one kind. We weren't afraid of God and we believed that He loved us all. We prayed to God and didn't have to worry about saying only certain words. Now Aunt Cathie has brought her nasty old God here and He gets mad at anybody who dares to smile. Nobody sings, or laughs in our house any more. Mamma and Aunt Bertha used to always be singing, laughing and happy. Now nobody dares because Aunt Cathie's God will get mad if they do. You can do what you want with me, Papa, but I'm not going to be a Catholic. I'm going to the Latter-Day Saint Sunday school and I'm going to be a Mormon."

Aunt Cathie pointed at Mamma. "Tena has poisoned the boy's mind against me."

Papa looked at Aunt Cathie. I'd never seen him so angry. "That is the cruelest and most unjust remark I have ever heard." Papa stood up, and this time he pointed at Aunt

Cathie. "How dare you say such a lie about my wife! Go to your room. Pray to God to forgive you for the manner in which you have distorted His divinity to a child. I'll never permit you to force religion upon my children. Their faith in religion must come from within."

Aunt Cathie's eyes blazed. "How dare you speak to your own sister in this manner? All the boy needs is a good old-fashioned whipping."

Papa's voice was hoarse as he said, "Go to your room, Cathie, before I say things I may later regret."

Aunt Cathie left the room and Papa sat down again. He looked at Tom. "My son," he said and must have been very moved to call Tom anything but T. D., "I have been very unjust to you and your mother. I just want to impress on you two things. First, that there is only one God and He is the Father of all the people. Second, that you do not judge all Catholics by your Aunt Cathie. I am a Catholic. Now," Papa looked around the room, "we will spend our Sunday evening as we did before Aunt Cathie came here. The first hymn we will sing will be 'Come, Come Ye Saints.' "

And that was how my brother Tom decided to be a Mormon. Sweyn, Katie, Earnie and I remained Catholics.

19

THE FALLEN WOMAN

I wasn't aware my Uncle Will lived with a mistress until one day he came to our house, and I knew something terrible was wrong when I saw him. He came into the hallway from the side porch, knocking the snow off his hat and coat. I was at the top of the stairs and he had a look on his face as if he'd seen a ghost. It was the first time I'd ever seen Uncle Will scared. I had thought that nothing in the world could scare my uncle.

He went into the kitchen, and I crept halfway down the stairs so I could hear.

"Princess," he said to Mamma, "I've never asked a favor and I wouldn't now if there was any other way out. Queenie is ill. Desperately ill. I think she is dying. There is no doctor in East Adenville. Please, Princess, see that Mormon Bishop. Tell him I need a doctor. I can't let her die. I love her." And Uncle Will the indestructible began to cry.

Mamma spoke briskly as she always did in a crisis. "Air out my bedroom, Bertha. Put on clean linen. Heat water. Will, go down to the corral and hitch the team to the wagon. When you are ready, come back and help me carry a mattress and blankets. Leave the seats out of the wagon."

"But, Princess," Uncle Will protested, "you can't just bring Queenie here."

"Of course we'll bring her here. You hurry up. Bertha, as soon as the bedroom is fixed, go get Dr. LeRoy."

Aunt Bertha shook her head. "I'd like to see the expression on Cathie's face when she finds out about this."

Mamma rode in the wagon with Uncle Will right up to the front of the Whitehorse Saloon. She marched right through the saloon. The customers, aware of Queenie's illness, all removed their hats out of respect to Mamma. They stood bareheaded until Mamma and Uncle Will, who was carrying Queenie wrapped in a blanket, came back down and went outside.

We children were watching out the upstairs bedroom window when the wagon stopped in front of our house, and saw Uncle Will carrying Queenie up the walk through the snow, her copper-colored hair sticking out from the white blanket.

Aunt Bertha and Dr. LeRoy arrived just as Mamma got Queenie settled in her bed. We heard Papa come in the front door; then Mamma's voice. "Will, you take a drink of brandy and lie down in Tom's bedroom."

We heard Uncle Will say, "I'll pass up the brandy, but I should lie down. I've been up three nights with her. Princess, you must promise me you'll call me if—" he fumbled for words.

"I promise to call you if Dr. LeRoy finds Queenie's condition grave."

We children were all crowded around the top of the stairs because Mamma had told us we couldn't come down. Tom motioned us back into the hallway. "Does anybody know what a fallen woman is?" he asked.

Sweyn scratched his ear. "I think it's one who falls down in the gutter drunk and can't get up."

"That's not right," Katie said. "A fallen woman is one who doesn't go to church. Why is Queenie a fallen woman, Tom?"

Tom shrugged. "I heard Aunt Cathie say one time that Uncle Will's housekeeper was a fallen woman. The way Aunt Cathie said it made it sound like something real bad. But Aunt Cathie thinks everybody is bad."

I began to wonder what Aunt Cathie would do when she returned from Castle Rock, where she was helping Father Caffarella do some work at the church. Uncle Mark had driven her there in his new buggy. It occurred to me then that Uncle Mark was always hanging around Aunt Cathie. He would meet her downtown and carry her bundles home; he would take her for buggy rides; he was teaching her to ride a saddle pony. I guessed that the only reason Uncle Mark was doing all these things was to get Aunt Cathie out of the house so that Mamma could have a little peace.

We were all afraid that we would have to go to bed that night before Aunt Cathie came back, but Mamma told us we could play in the parlor if we kept very quiet. Uncle Mark escorted Aunt Cathie to the door and said good night. Mamma put a finger to her lips and motioned for Aunt Cathie to follow her into the dining room. We could hear Mamma whispering.

Then all of a sudden we heard Aunt Cathie. "Do you mean to tell me, Tena, that you've permitted that worthless, sinful brother of mine to bring that harlot into this house?"

Mamma's voice was very firm. "Will you please have the decency to be quiet when a person is lying at death's door?"

"I will not be quiet," Aunt Cathie shouted. "If you think

for a moment I'll remain under the same roof as that fallen woman, or permit you to let innocent children be contaminated by her presence, you're mistaken. In the name of God and decency, you must make her leave at once. How dare you do such a brazen, sinful thing?"

Papa got up from his rocking chair just as Uncle Will came out of Papa's bedroom, rubbing sleep from his eyes. They both started for the dining room and then stopped as they heard Mamma.

"Now you listen to me, Cathie. To my everlasting shame I permitted you to drive my own father and mother from my home. I'll not make the same mistake again. You may think you are a good Catholic, but you're not. To be a good Catholic, a good Mormon, a good Methodist, a good Baptist, you must first be a good Christian. Christ did not scorn Mary Magdalene. Christ taught that compassion, kindness, charity, humility, tolerance and love were the mark of a good Christian. I've yet to see any of these virtues in you. I've been very patient with you. I've permitted you to dictate to me in my own home. I've allowed you to humiliate me. But this time, you've gone too far. Queenie will not only remain in this house until she is well, but will also be a welcome guest whenever she cares to visit me after she recovers. If I hear you say one more word against her, you'll have to leave my house."

"Then, I most certainly shall leave," Aunt Cathie declared.

"Bertha will help you pack in the morning," Mamma said quietly.

Papa and Uncle Will walked into the dining room. "Thomas, my own brother," Aunt Cathie cried out, "are you going to permit Tena to speak to me in this manner?"

"Tena is right," Papa said. "Your intolerance has become

an obsession with you, Cathie. I do not believe you are well mentally. You have given not only the children but Tena a very distorted picture of Catholicism. I think it best you leave. Will and I will defray your expenses to Boylestown and provide you with a suitable income for as long as you live."

Aunt Cathie turned white and then ran sobbing from the room. Mamma looked at Papa and said, "Thank you, Tom dear." Aunt Bertha who had come out of the bedroom and heard most of the argument raised her hands above her head and cried, "Hallelujah!"

A few minutes later Old Lady Miller showed up with her black satchel. Mamma greeted her in the parlor. "I was hoping you would come," she said.

Mrs. Miller smiled at Mamma. "You certainly didn't think I might not come, knowing who it is that is ill, did you, Tena?"

"Not for a moment," Mamma said.

The next morning Aunt Cathie came down to breakfast, her eyes red from weeping. "There are some important things I must say to you, Tena," she said.

Mamma shook her head. "I'd rather you didn't say them in front of the children."

"I'd prefer to say them in front of everybody," Aunt Cathie said as she looked around the table. "I'm not going home. I'm going to a Catholic retreat."

Tom, never a bashful one, asked, "What's a retreat?"

For the first time my brother won a winsome smile from Aunt Cathie. "A retreat," she explained, "is a period of time spent in silence, prayer, and hearing religious lectures, usually for a period of a week or longer, during which one examines one's conscience and soul to try and become a better Christian, spiritually, morally and physically."

Tom shook his head, "You sure need it, Aunt Cathie," he said, but instead of getting angry at him, she smiled.

"I do, Tom." It was the first time she'd called him that. "After I leave the retreat I shall spend a long time in meditation and prayer until I've found the answer to many things."

Mamma smiled at her. "I hope you find the answers, Cathie."

Aunt Cathie leaned back and shut her eyes. "I'll seek the answers to many things, Tena. Such as why you have always frightened me. That surprises you, doesn't it, Tena? How you, in your quiet way, could frighten me? I must know why every strange dog that sees you wags its tail and follows you home. I must know why everybody in this town, from the Mormon Bishop down to the lowest drunkard, loves you. I must know why people when they mention your name seem to speak it as if they were speaking the name of a saint. I must know what it is that makes everybody love you and want to be your friend, except myself. When I have found the answers to these questions, then I shall return."

Mamma's eyes dimmed with tears. "When you find these answers, Cathie, as you will find them through prayer and God, you will find me as eager for your friendship and affection as I'll be to give you mine. God bless you, Cathie."

Queenie was ill for a long, long time. Mrs. Miller, Mamma or Aunt Bertha had to be with her all the time for several days. It was almost four weeks before we children were even permitted to see her. Mamma was beautiful like a flower. Queenie was beautiful like the sunrise. Mamma had fixed Queenie's copper-colored hair with a pretty ribbon, and she was wearing Mamma's best bed jacket. She looked pale, but she smiled as we children trooped into the bedroom.

Tom walked boldly up to the bed. "I'm T. D. Fitzgerald," he introduced himself. "I'm sure happy to see you're getting better, Miss Queenie. I brought you a present." He opened his hand and showed her the present. "It's a genuine guaranteed Indian arrowhead."

She seemed very serious and inspected the arrowhead closely. "It is a fine specimen," she said, "not Paiute, but Apache. I'll treasure it forever." How she could tell, I didn't know. But I did know that the cattleman, Mr. Wade, had brought Tom the arrowhead from Texas, and it was Apache.

Sweyn stepped up to the bed next. He introduced himself and gave Queenie his own personal copy of *David Copperfield*.

Katie gave Queenie her favorite hair ribbon. Queenie removed the one Mamma had placed in her hair and put on Katie's.

Earnie gave her one of his crayon drawings in a natural pine-wood frame.

After all these wonderful gifts, I was a little ashamed. But I stepped up to the bed, and introduced myself. "My present is a play I've written. It will be acted out on our front porch when you are well enough to see it."

Queenie began crying. Mamma came into the room and shooed us all out. As we went upstairs, Tom was shaking his head. "You don't suppose she thought we gave her the presents just because she got rid of Aunt Cathie for us, do you?

Maybe we ought to tell her that Aunt Cathie didn't have anything to do with it."

The day Queenie was well enough to be moved to the front porch was a big occasion. I overheard Queenie say to Mamma, "I can't let you do it, Mrs. Fitzgerald. God knows, I've disgraced you enough. Just give me a few more days and I'll be well enough to go home."

"Stuff and nonsense," Mamma answered. "It is a lovely spring day. The snow has melted and the sun is shining. The doctor said you need fresh air. So, out you go. And remember, dear, the only person more embarrassed than a person being stared at, is the person staring—providing you stare right back."

Then Queenie began to cry. "You're so good. You are like an angel. How can I tell you how much I care for you? How can I ever tell you about me?"

"There isn't a thing I don't know about you," Mamma said. "While you were delirious you told me all about yourself."

"You mean you still let me stay here after that?"

"Yes, Queenie, and not because of pity. Not because I felt it my duty to my husband's brother. Not because of any of the reasons you may think. I did it because I know you are a good woman. I mean good in the way I believe Christ thought about good. I know you love Will very much. That alone makes you and me very good friends. I'll never let anybody in this town hurt you. Now, up you get, and out to the porch you go."

A curious few did pass our house. Tom, Earnie, Sweyn

and I began turning somersaults and playing leapfrog on the lawn, so if anybody stopped to stare, Queenie would think they were watching us. When Tom began imitating town characters like Windy Davis, we heard Queenie laugh for the first time—a deep, throaty laugh.

I didn't feel justified in calling upon Mamma to help me with my first play.* I felt that since it was a present to Queenie, I should do it myself; but I ran into so many difficulties that I compromised by asking Tom to assist me. He agreed to cast, direct, edit and act in my play without charge because it was a present for Queenie. We rehearsed in the barn.

My play opened one afternoon about two-thirty. We'd hung bed sheets across the front porch to shield the players and the audience from spectators in the street; and we arranged the stage part of the porch so that we could use the parlor for a dressing room and make our entrances and exits from its door.

We played to a capacity audience consisting of Mamma, Queenie, Aunt Bertha, Mrs. Miller, Mrs. Fransen, Mrs. Lee, Papa, Uncle Will, Uncle Mark, Marshal Gentry, Judge Baker, Windy Davis, and about fifteen kids.

The play opened with Sweyn stepping before the curtain which consisted of bed sheets hung on a clothesline wire across the porch. "Ladies and gentlemen," Sweyn said, "I take great pleasure in bringing to you for the first time in Adenville theatrical history a play entitled *The Fallen Woman,* written by our home-town playwright, J. D. Fitzgerald. It was directed and produced by that great impres-

---

* After my mother's death I found the pages of this play, along with other youthful literary efforts, sealed in a big fruit jar in a trunk in our attic. Consequently I quote from the text itself.

sario, T. D. Fitzgerald. The sterling cast includes myself, S. D. Fitzgerald, Katie Fitzgerald, E. D. Dawson, T. D. Fitzgerald and J. D. Fitzgerald. Ladies and gentlemen, it is curtain time."

Sweyn pulled back the curtain revealing the stage. One of Mamma's old dressmaking forms lay in the center of the stage. I stood at one side of the stage, and raised my arms.

"The woman has fallen," I recited. "Will nobody help the poor fallen woman?" I cupped my hand to my ear. "Hark, someone is coming. Maybe it is somebody who'll help the poor fallen woman."

Katie, dressed in some of Mamma's old clothes and high-heeled shoes, came out of the parlor doorway on cue. With her nose in the air she walked over to the dress-form and looked disdainfully at the fallen woman. "I am the Countess Catherine and I will not help the fallen woman. Let her stay on the cold, cold ground." Katie swept up her skirts and made her exit.

It was so sad and beautiful that tears were streaming down my face. Again I held up my arms. "The Countess Catherine will not help the poor fallen woman. Is there no mercy, no pity, in this wide, wide world? Hark!" I again held my hand to my ear, "Someone is coming." I shielded my eyes with my hand and looked toward the parlor door. "Behold, it is an Indian Chief. Maybe he will help the poor fallen woman."

Earnie, dressed in Tom's Indian war bonnet and an Indian blanket, came onto the stage. His brightly painted face didn't change expression as he spoke his lines. "Ugh. Me Chief Black Cloud. Squaw fall down. Leave 'em squaw on the cold, cold ground." He made his exit.

My voice shook with emotion as I cried out: "The woman is fallen and nobody will help her, not even an Indian." I

held my hand to my ear. "Hark! I hear the sound of barking dogs. Someone is coming. Oh, pray that it is somebody
who will help the poor fallen woman."

Sweyn came out of our parlor doorway, wearing one of
Papa's discarded black beaver hats, a pair of Papa's old trousers, and a worn checkered vest which hung down over his
hips. He held two ropes tied to the necks of two of our dogs.
This dramatic piece of directing by my brother had caused
me to rewrite the scene; there had been no dogs in the original script. Sweyn stroked his mustache made from hairs
we had pulled out of the tail of one of our horses. "I am the
villain, Black-Hearted Dalton. Aha!" he cried as he pointed
at the fallen woman. "At last I've found you and now you
will pay for trying to escape from my clutches. My bloodhounds will tear you to pieces." He laughed fiendishly as
he let the dogs get near the fallen woman. Again Tom's
powerful stagecraft came into play; he'd placed soup bones
and ground meat inside the dressmaker's dummy. The dogs
began barking and biting at it.

I was crying so hard by now it was difficult for me to speak
my lines. Piteously I raised my arms. "The poor fallen
woman is too ill to fight off the bloodhounds. They will tear
her to pieces." I clasped my hands in prayer. "Please, God,
save the poor fallen woman. Save her before it is too late.
Hark!" I held my hand to my ear. "I hear the sound of galloping hoofs coming closer and closer. Will the hero arrive
in time to save the poor fallen woman from being torn to
pieces by the bloodhounds?"

After completing the sound effects by hitting two blocks
of wood together, Tom made his dramatic entrance. He
wore a cowboy hat, the buckskin suit Uncle Will had given
him for Christmas, and a leather holster with a wood pistol
in it. "Whoa!" he shouted as he pulled on the rope tied to

the end of a broomstick he was astride. "Whoa, my trusty steed! Whoa, boy!" He looked at Black-Hearted Dalton, then at the fallen woman. "What deviltry is this I see?" he demanded.

Black-Hearted Dalton shrugged. "It is nothing. Just a fallen woman that my bloodhounds are tearing to pieces."

"Call off your dogs, you blood-thirsty villain," Tom shouted.

The villain sneered. "Who do you think you are, giving me orders?"

"I am Tex Goodheart, Indian scout, buffalo hunter, rodeo champion and Captain of the United States Army. Aha, you black-hearted villain, I see you know me because you tremble with fear."

"I know, you, Tex Goodheart, but I'm not afraid. We'll shoot it out fair and square. I'll count three and then we'll draw."

I put my hand to my mouth in an aside to the audience. "Does Tex Goodheart know how cowardly Black-Hearted Dalton really is? The villain knows he cannot outdraw Tex Goodheart fair and square. He will draw at the count of two and kill Tex Goodheart, then there will be nobody to save the poor fallen woman."

The villain put his hand on the butt of his pistol. "I'm counting, Tex Goodheart," he said, "we'll draw on the count of three. One, two—"

As the villain tried to draw at the count of two, Tex Goodheart pulled the wooden gun from its holster and shouted, "Bang!" He returned the gun to its holster. "Thought you'd catch Tex Goodheart with that old one," he said as the villain staggered and fell. "That trick was tried on Tex Goodheart before, when he was Marshal at Dodge City."

The dogs broke away when Sweyn fell down, and ran through the audience and off the porch. Tex Goodheart ad-libbed, "It's a good thing they ran away. I hate killing a dog, even a mean one." He guided his broomstick horse over to the dressmaker's dummy, picked the dummy up in his arms. "Fear not, fallen woman," he said, "Tex Goodheart is here. Tex Goodheart has picked you up from the cold, cold ground. Tex Goodheart will protect you and never, never let you fall down again. You don't have to worry, Ma'am. You have the word of Tex Goodheart, Indian scout, buffalo hunter, rodeo champion and Captain of the United States Army."

As our hero rode off the stage, I held out my hands toward the audience and shouted, "The fallen woman is saved. The moral of the play is that when you fall down, have faith because somebody who is brave, good and kind will pick you up, if you just have faith."

I knew my play was a great success from the thunderous applause. Queenie was so overcome that she was chewing on her handkerchief. Uncle Will and the men were laughing uncontrollably, but I knew they were doing it only because they were men and didn't want to be seen shedding tears. As we made our curtain calls, the adults and kids booed Countess Catherine, Chief Black Cloud, and Black-Hearted Dalton. There was wild applause for Tex Goodheart. There weren't any cries for the author, but I took a few bows anyway.

The day finally came when Queenie had completely recovered. We all felt sad about her departure. Queenie was a boy's dream of a friend. She never talked down to us, and when she was well enough, she'd put on a pair of overalls and play ball, or any other game, with us.

The night before Queenie was to leave Uncle Will came to supper. After we had been sent to bed, I woke up thirsty and went to the head of the stairs to call to Mamma that I wanted a drink of water. Then I heard Uncle Will's voice in the kitchen.

"Why all the mystery, Princess?"

Mamma's voice was soft but I could hear. "Queenie is well enough to leave, Will, but she isn't going back to the Whitehorse with you."

"Just a minute, Princess," Uncle Will laughed. "I'll save you from making a speech. I have the license. Hal Gentry is going to keep Judge Baker sober tomorrow. I bought the Jenkins place right next to Dr. LeRoy's. I'd be afraid to try marriage if it wasn't for you, Princess. It may take time, but with you on Queenie's side we'll make it. I never knew how much I loved her until I thought I was going to lose her."

"It'll be hard for a while," Mamma said, "but once folks know the real Queenie, they'll love her. And speaking of you being ahead of me, I started making Queenie's wedding gown a week after we brought her here."

After Uncle Will and Queenie got married there were a lot of people in West Adenville who still considered Queenie a fallen woman; there were more who became her friends. Mrs. Miller became Queenie's staunchest champion, and in time Queenie became one of the pillars of Adenville society.

20

UNCLE WILL LOSES A WAGER

THE TRAVELING EVANGELISTS of the Old West were as much
a part of it as the cowboys and Indians. Most of these men of
the gospel had a camp wagon which opened at the rear like
a platform. They carried hymn books which they distributed to the crowd at their services, usually held at the camp
ground. Proselytizing in those days was graphic. All sinners
were consigned to burn in everlasting Hell unless they re-
pented.

The preachers also traveled from farm to farm, and from
ranch to ranch, in the outlying sections. All work would
stop for as long as a week, during which time the evangelist
instilled enough fear of the Lord into the family and hired
men to last them until his next trip.

In East Adenville Windy Davis was always the first one to
fall on his knees, confess his sins and ask to be saved. Windy's
only trouble was that he felt so good after these spiritual
baths that he headed for the nearest saloon to celebrate his
salvation.

Reverend Herbert Holcomb, a big man with red hair,
grew tired of this gypsy existence and decided he wanted to
remain in East Adenville. The reason he picked on Uncle

Will's saloon was never known, unless it was that the White-horse was the largest in town. The preacher stood in front of the Whitehorse day after day, calling down the wrath of the Lord on Uncle Will and all other purveyors of sin and alcohol. He stopped only long enough to enter the Whitehorse Saloon and partake of the free meal there three times a day.

The preacher began to get on people's nerves. Uncle Will decided to fight fire with fire. He approached Reverend Holcomb one day. "It just doesn't seem right and proper for a preacher like you to have to spread the word of the Gospel in the middle of the street. I've been thinking it over. But I don't want to make a mistake. I'll make you a proposition. We'll draw a circle in the middle of the street. If you can remain inside that circle and preach the Gospel for twenty-four hours without once stopping, I'll build you a church. If you leave the circle once during the twenty-four hours, or stop preaching the Gospel, you give me your word you'll leave town."

The Reverend Holcomb agreed to the bargain. The test was to begin at ten o'clock the next morning. When Uncle Will told his friends about it, Dandy Allen studied one of his big amethyst cuff links. "Why don't you just run him out of town? Or just get the other saloon keepers and yourself to stop him from eating the free lunches and starve him out of town?"

"Can't do it," Uncle Will shrugged. "The Reverend Holcomb is a Methodist and Bertha Tuttle is a Methodist. You don't know Bertha. She'd take my hide off me. Anyway, this is going to be a lot of fun."

The next morning there was a crowd in the Whitehorse Saloon as news of the testing of the preacher got around. A circle was drawn in the middle of the street. At exactly ten o'clock the Reverend Holcomb entered it, opened his Bible and began to preach.

The first test came when Lefty Jackson staggered out of the Whitehorse Saloon pretending he was drunk. He pulled his gun and shouted at the preacher, "Dance, you Jesus-man, or I'll shoot your toes off." Lefty began shooting, bringing up puffs of dust within inches of Reverend Holcomb's feet. The evangelist didn't move anything but his mouth. "The Lord is my shepherd and shall watch over me."

The next test thought up by Uncle Will and his friends came when Marshal Gentry ran down the street, yelling: "Everybody inside. Frenchy Dumaine is gunning for Al Wilson." He stopped in front of the Whitehorse Saloon. "Reverend, get inside or you'll be killed. I order you off the street." But the evangelist kept right on preaching.

Frenchy Dumaine with a gun in each hand came down the street. He stopped a few feet from the preacher. "Whar ees thees peeg who try to steal Frenchy Dumaine's girl?"

Al Wilson stepped from around the Whitehorse Saloon. "Here I am, you yellow dog. Come a-gunning."

Uncle Will came out the door of his saloon. "Get out of the way, you damn fool," he shouted at the preacher. But Holcomb didn't move. He raised his face toward the sky and kept right on preaching.

Frenchy let go with a couple of shots, one of which put a hole in the preacher's coat and the other missed the man's face by inches. Al Wilson pulled the trigger of his gun. The gun battle blazed with the Reverend Holcomb standing between the two men until Al Wilson grabbed his stomach and pitched forward on his face.

Frenchy holstered his guns. "By gar," he shouted, "I keel any man who dare look at my Francine."

Marshal Gentry came out of the saloon with a blanket

which he placed over Wilson. He waited with Uncle Will and several others until Pete Veeder, who collected five dollars from the saloon keepers every time he picked up a body and dug a grave, came down the street in his wagon. The body was lifted into the wagon. With a straight face Uncle Will walked over to the preacher. "I'm having Wilson put in my ice house so the body will keep until tomorrow. Want you to hold a funeral service for him."

"The Lord giveth and the Lord taketh away," the Reverend Holcomb said and went on with his preaching.

It was late afternoon before the next test. Johnny Lane, a cowboy, came riding his horse at a gallop, shouting: "Run for it! Runaway team! Runaway team!"

Not far behind him a big freighter pulled by four horses at a gallop thundered down the street, headed straight for the Reverend Holcomb. From the safety of the wooden sidewalk the crowd in front of the Whitehorse Saloon saw the preacher's face blanch as he shouted: "Oh Lord, give me strength. Ye of little faith behold the power of the Lord."

The driver, who was in complete control of the horses, swerved the lead team just in time. The freighter roared past the preacher, missing him by inches.

By nightfall the Whitehorse Saloon was jammed. Bets were being made on each test. The carting away of Al Wilson's supposedly dead body had been a build-up for a test to come. His Francine, a dance hall girl working in the Whitehorse, ran into the street and threw herself at the preacher's feet. "I've listened to you from my upstairs window. I want to be saved. Oh, save me, preacher man, from a life of sin. Save me from that brute Frenchy Dumaine. I'd rather be dead than to go on being his woman. Save me."

Frenchy reeled out of the Whitehorse feigning drunkenness. "By gar," he shouted pulling his guns, "I keel wan man today because he try to take my Francine. Now, by Gar, I keel thees preacher too."

"Please, Frenchy, don't shoot!" Francine pleaded on her knees. "You can't kill a preacher man. I'll do anything you ask. Please spare his life."

Frenchy considered for a moment. "Thees preacher man I know you do not love, but he put crazy ideas een your head. I geev heem five minutes to get outa town. Eef he no go, I keel heem, preacher or no preacher."

As Frenchy went back into the saloon, Francine begged Reverend Holcomb to leave town. "Please go. He will kill you just like he killed Al. I can't bear to have any more bloodshed on my hands."

Reverend Holcomb kept right on preaching. "He who liveth by the sword shall perish by the sword, saith the Lord."

Marshal Gentry came out of the saloon. "Take my advice, parson, and leave town. Frenchy is crazy drunk. I can't arrest him for anything until after he kills you." He turned as Frenchy came through the doors of the saloon. "Run for it, parson!" Gentry shouted.

The Reverend didn't run. "The Lord will protect me," he said and went right on with his preaching. Frenchy sent bullets whistling within inches of the evangelist's head. Finally in disgust he holstered his guns. "By Gar, I cannot keel a preacher man."

Uncle Will sat at the big stake poker table with his friends. It was Judge Baker who suggested the next test. "The Reverend Holcomb just doesn't scare physically," he said rubbing his porous red nose. "We must devise a test that would appeal to his moral fiber. Something like a good woman in distress."

Five minutes after the eight-thirty train from Salt Lake arrived that night, a dance hall girl, primly dressed and without makeup, accompanied by a new faro dealer who was dressed like a cowboy, approached the Reverend Holcomb. "Pardon me, sir," the faro dealer said. "My wife and I are just returning from our honeymoon in Salt Lake. We were supposed to be met by friends to drive us out to the ranch. I learned at the depot that a storm caused a landslide in Pinto Canyon and our friends can't get through. We must remain here overnight. Can you recommend a good respectable hotel?"

Reverend Holcomb continued with his preaching the gospel as he pointed toward the Sheepman's Hotel. The faro dealer looked at his mythical bride. "I know you are tired, dear. I'll walk back to the depot and get our luggage. You can wait here."

When the faro dealer was out of sight, two cowboys came out of the Allies Saloon, pretending they were drunk. They looked at the girl. "Wa-al, Jim!" one of them said as they leered at the girl. "Look what I found, and purty as a picture. Never see such a purty dance hall girl."

The girl screamed. "I'm a respectable married woman. Stay away from me."

One of the cowboys grabbed the girl and held his hand over her mouth. "Ain't no respectable woman caterwaulin' around the streets this time of night." The two men dragged the girl toward the alley by the side of the Whitehorse Saloon. In a few moments agonized screams from the girl pierced the night air. "Help me! Save me! For God's sake, please save me, save me!"

The Reverend Holcomb remained inside the circle, preaching. The girl, the two cowboys and the faro dealer entered the Whitehorse Saloon by the back way to report failure.

The testing of Reverend Holcomb continued until midnight, when fate took a hand. Fire broke out in the Prairie Restaurant just two buildings from the Whitehorse Saloon. The buildings were all made of wood, and the wind soon spread the fire to the building next to the Whitehorse Saloon. Bucket brigades were quickly formed. The Mormons sent fifty men from West Adenville to help. The wind was blowing northward, and Marshal Gentry pointed out to Uncle Will that there wasn't a chance of stopping the blaze from reaching the Whitehorse Saloon. Papa, Uncle Will, Uncle Mark and others began carrying the most valuable things from the Whitehorse Saloon.

The Reverend Holcomb was the only person not helping fight the fire or remove articles from buildings in the path of the blaze. He remained inside the circle, preaching.

Uncle Will passed him several times as he was carrying things from the Whitehorse. One time he stopped and spoke to the evangelist, "This wasn't my idea, Reverend, but it looks like you'll lose the bet. When the fire reaches my saloon, you'll either have to move or be burned to death."

The preacher clasped his hands over his Bible, and raised his face toward the sky. "Oh merciful Lord, heed the prayer of thy humble servant. Grant to him the means of a place of worship that he may deify Thy glory and save sinners in Thy name. Thou hast the power, Oh Lord, to still the waves of the seas, direct the heavenly bodies of the universe. The rain, the snow, the wind all acknowledge Thy divine mastery. I beseech Thee, Oh Lord, to change the wind. And if it is not Thy will, then I shall stand here, on this spot while the flames consume me, shouting my praises unto Thee."

Uncle Will was the only one who heard that prayer. The fire fighters, both Mormon and Gentile, had given up the bucket brigade. The whole block was doomed unless the wind changed. Just before the flames reached hungrily for the wood of the Whitehorse Saloon, the wind suddenly changed and began blowing southward. A great shout arose from the crowd as the bucket brigade was resumed. If the wind continued blowing southward, they knew, they could save the Whitehorse Saloon and other buildings.

At ten o'clock the next morning, Reverend Holcomb stepped out of the circle to the applause of many onlookers.

Uncle Will bought a lot in West Adenville, and a Methodist church was built upon it with small living quarters in the rear. The Latter-Day Saints donated an old organ.

The first Sunday service the church was filled almost to capacity. Catholics, Methodists, Baptists, and apostate Mormons attended. A dumpy little woman named Mrs. Watts played the organ, while her son pumped it. Aunt Bertha passed out hymnals, and her joyful voice led the singing of Methodist hymns.

Our whole family attended the first service. Uncle Will brought Aunt Queenie; Judge Baker, Hal Gentry, Windy Davis, and even Dandy Allen and his girl Marie were there. We were all expecting a sermon of gratitude to Uncle Will for his generosity in building the church. Instead, the big red-headed preacher mounted the pulpit and said many uncomplimentary things about my uncle, among them:

"God is not mocked. For whatever a man soweth, that shall he also reap. Ye came to hear me praise Will Fitzgerald for his generosity in providing this church, instead ye shall hear me flay him for his sinfulness. Ye cannot buy your way into the Kingdom of Heaven. God forgives those who trespass against Him, but only if they are truly repentant. Ye cannot speak out of two sides of your mouth. Ye cannot praise the Lord one day and take His name in vain the rest of the week. Ye cannot accumulate wealth as a pur-

veyor of sin and wickedness and buy your way into the Kingdom of Heaven, no matter how many churches you build.
For he that soweth of his flesh shall of the flesh reap corrup-
tion. Will Fitzgerald did not build this church. The Lord
built it and gave it to me. There is no place in this congregation for sinners and hypocrites unless they are truly repentant. Not until Will Fitzgerald sells his den of iniquity
and cries out in public for God's forgiveness shall he be welcome here."

There was more, but at this point Uncle Will burst out
laughing. He was immediately joined by Marshal Gentry,
Judge Baker, Windy Davis and Dandy Allen.

Uncle Will stood up. "Forgive the interruption, Reverend. I'll save you the trouble of casting me out of the temple as the Pharisees were. There is one thing I admire about
you, Reverend. You are consistent." Still laughing, Uncle
Will and his friends from East Adenville filed out of the
church.

After the services, Mamma didn't seem to think that Reverend Holcomb had been very tolerant or kind. But Papa
laughed about it all the way home and duly reported the
sermon in his newspaper, from which I have copied it.

The following Sunday the congregation had thinned
down to Aunt Bertha and about a dozen other people. A
man of lesser stature than Reverend Holcomb might have
given up. Bold as brass, he marched into the Whitehorse
Saloon the next day, where he found Uncle Will standing at
the bar with Marshal Gentry. "In time," Reverend Holcomb
said, "the town will grow and my pews will be filled with
devout parishioners. Until such a time, I need financial as-
sistance."

Uncle Will leaned back against the bar and hooked his
thumbs in the belt of his jeweled holster. "Are you serious,

Reverend? After what you said about me? Do you mean to
tell me that the money I make from this 'den of iniquity'
may be tainted but not tainted enough to stop you from
taking it?"

"I do not seek charity," he preacher replied. "I seek only
a position that will pay me enough remuneration to keep
body and soul together."

Uncle Will smiled. "I could use a faro dealer, Reverend,
but how do I know you are capable?"

"Do not jest with me," Reverend Holcomb said defiantly.
"The Lord tells me that my destiny is somehow tied to you.
Why, I do not know. I do not question it. I am a capable
bookkeeper and accountant. I know you can obtain employment for me that will pay me enough to keep myself alive
until my congregation grows."

Uncle Will slapped his knee. "I'm going to take you up
on that. I have a lot of bookkeeping and accounting work.
The other saloon keepers have the same problem. If I can
arrange for you to do this work, it will take about one day a
week for each saloon. Will you accept?"

"The Lord will understand," Reverend Holcomb replied.

So the Reverend Herbert Holcomb went to work for the
saloon keepers of East Adenville. He retained this position
for several years, during which time his church gradually became known as a community church and all denominations attended except the Catholics and the Mormons.

21

PRELUDE TO MURDER

I CANNOT REMEMBER a time during my childhood when we had fewer than four dogs, and sometimes we had as many as ten. Every time any bitch in town had a litter of pups you could almost bet that one or more would end up at our home. Mamma found homes for the dogs with sheepmen and cattlemen and ranchers who visited us.

I learned a very important lesson about dogs when I was a child. I was being punished for trampling down some of Mamma's flowers when I had carelessly run through her flower bed. I was feeling sorry for myself and perhaps that was why I tried to take it out on one of our dogs. While I was sitting on our back porch playing with him, I grabbed his ear and twisted it. The dog yelped with pain. I twisted the ear again, and again the dog yelped. Mamma opened the back door but didn't say a word.

That night right in the middle of supper, Mamma got up from her place and walked around behind me. She grabbed my ear and twisted it until tears came into my eyes. Papa and the rest looked at Mamma with astonishment; but she didn't say a word, just went back to her place and resumed eating.

After supper, when I was sitting on the parlor floor playing, Mamma laid aside her embroidery work, leaned over, grabbed my ear and twisted it until I cried: "Please, Mamma. I'm getting the silent treatment. Isn't that enough punishment for ruining your flowers?"

Papa put down the book he was reading and looked at Mamma. "The boy deserves an explanation, Tena girl."

Mamma merely shook her head. "I know what I'm doing."

I went over and laid my head in Mamma's lap. "Please, Mamma, forgive me for trampling on your flowers."

To my consternation she grabbed my ear and twisted it again. I rushed over to Papa.

"Holy Jupiter!" Papa shouted. "What is this nonsense?"

Mamma beckoned to me. I approached her cautiously with my hands over my ears.

She smiled at me. "You know I love you, don't you, John D.?"

When I nodded, she continued. "Then perhaps you'll understand how Spot felt this afternoon. He knew you loved him and couldn't understand why you hurt him by twisting his ear. The first time he thought you'd just made a mistake. But when you did it the second time, the poor dog couldn't understand why his master who loved him was hurting him. Now, if you'll promise never to hurt another animal, I'll forgive you."

One of the most terrifying cries to hear when I was a boy was that of "Mad dog." The streets would empty as if by magic. The men would take their rifles and solemnly bid goodbye to their families.

The day our dog Ranger went mad, I was playing with Howard Kay in our backyard. Ranger was acting funny, running around in circles trying to bite his tail and vomiting. I went in to tell Mamma.

Mamma's face turned white, but she was moving even before I finished telling her. She took a rifle from the gun rack, put a shell into it and rushed to the back porch.

Howard Kay was laughing and pointing at Ranger. "Look at old Ranger, he's got a white mustache."

"Don't move, Howard," Mamma shouted, just as Ranger growled and prepared to spring at Howard. Mamma put the rifle to her shoulder. There was the loud bang of the exploding shell. Ranger's four legs flattened out in mid-air and he dropped dead at Howard's feet. Mamma put down the rifle and leaned against the porch banister. "Oh Lord, I thank thee," she whispered.

Uncle Mark said it was one of the best free-hand shots with a rifle within his memory. Mamma had caught Ranger right between the eyes while he was in the air. If she'd hit him anywhere else he'd have lived long enough to bite Howard. Mamma said it was the Good Lord aiming the rifle, not she.

There was one dog in East Adenville that everybody despised. It was a big white English bulldog owned by Dan Harkess, proprietor of the Allies Saloon. The dog's name was John Bull, and he was a killer. All the kids in West Adenville worried about their dogs straying into East Adenville. Dan Harkess had a big collar with brass rivets made for John Bull, which gave the dog an unfair advantage in a fight. For a while Harkess held dog fights in a barn in East Adenville and men bet on these. Most of the time they just bet on the time it would take John Bull to kill the other dog.

When Bishop Aden learned of these dog fights he went to Papa and told him such cruelty must be stopped. Papa spoke to Uncle Will about it. Uncle Will and Marshal Gentry informed Harkess that if the fights didn't stop they would take away his license and run him out of town.

This didn't stop Harkess from sicking John Bull on any dog running around loose in the streets of East Adenville. There were plenty of people who would have poisoned or shot John Bull, but they couldn't get near the dog without his master; Harkess kept the dog by his side all the time.

Brownie was the first dog I ever owned who wasn't a mongrel. He was a purebred Alaskan that Henri Dussiere had given me for my birthday. A strange dog, he didn't run and play with other dogs. My brothers said he was a snob. We tried to mate him when he was older, but he just stuck up his nose at all the bitches in town.

I didn't know Brownie could fight until he was about two years old. Frank Davis had a sheep dog with long shaggy hair that could lick any dog but John Bull. Frank was always picking on me because I wouldn't let Brownie fight his dog. One day Frank goaded me into letting the dogs fight. I knew the sheep dog wasn't a killer; he just chewed other dogs until they ran yelping away. The reason it was hard for a dog to fight the sheep dog was his long shaggy hair.

I thought Brownie was a coward when Frank yelled sic'im at his dog. Brownie stood as if bored until the sheep dog was almost on top of him, then he whirled and grabbed the sheep dog's rear leg. There was a crunching sound. Frank's dog began to whine as he pulled himself with his broken leg toward his master.

Frank shook his fist at me. "Now we'll have to shoot Shep. I'll get you for this, John."

"You hit me," I said, "and I'll have my brother Tom beat the daylights out of you." Frank was bigger than I.

But a dog that could fight in those days was like a gunman with a reputation. Brownie knew how to fight only one way. He'd get hold of the other dog's legs and break them. After this had happened a few times, all the owners of dogs in West Adenville left Brownie alone.

One afternoon I was playing hide and seek on the big bags of wool near the sheep-shearing pens by the railway tracks. Brownie had followed me, as he did wherever I went.

One of the sheep shearers saw Brownie. "That's a fine-looking dog you got there, boy."

I couldn't help bragging. "He's a thoroughbred and he can lick any dog in town."

A few minutes later Howard Kay shouted at me. "Run, John, and take Brownie with you." He was pointing toward East Adenville.

Dan Harkess and about ten other men were walking toward me. Harkess was leading John Bull with a chain. The saloon keeper was a tall man with a fierce, black, curlicued mustache. I didn't see why I should run. I was on my own side of the tracks.

Harkess looked at Brownie who was standing beside me. "So that's the dog that can lick any dog in town?"

"You leave my dog alone or I'll tell my Papa."

"I'm not going to hurt your dog, sonny. Why, I wouldn't think of letting John Bull fight a dog that was a coward."

"Brownie's not a coward," I shouted.

"If he isn't a coward, why not let him fight John Bull?"

I was ready to burst into tears when I saw Howard Kay come running back with Uncle Mark. Harkess threw back his head and jeered, "Some dog! Needs a Marshal to protect it." The men with Harkess began to laugh and make fun of Brownie.

Uncle Mark looked at me. "I can't decide this for you, John. We'll wait until your Uncle Will gets here." Then he looked at Harkess. "You boys are on the wrong side of the tracks. You can walk back or be carried back, and you'll be the first one to be carried, Harkess. Wait on the East Adenville side until the boy's uncle gets here."

The men muttered, but they went back across the tracks.

Uncle Will followed by Marshal Gentry, Judge Baker and Windy Davis were coming up the street. When they reached me, Uncle Will put his hand on my shoulder. "John," he said, "this had to happen sooner or later. If you don't let Brownie fight John Bull now, when he'll get a fair fight, Brownie might have to fight him later when nobody is around to see that Harkess takes the collar off John Bull."

I was trembling. "Brownie is no coward."

"Fine, John." Then he walked across the tracks with me following him. "Take off the collar," he said to Harkess. "And just to make it interesting, I'll bet five hundred in gold that my nephew's dog wins."

Harkess grinned. "You've got yourself a bet," he said as he knelt and unfastened the collar.

The men made a circle to give the dogs room to fight. Harkess said something to John Bull and the bulldog waddled toward Brownie. When John Bull got close enough he made a dive for Brownie's throat. Brownie jumped sideways just in time and moved around in back of John Bull so fast he was just a blur. I heard a crunching, cracking sound. Brownie jumped away just in time to be missed by John Bull's jaws as the bulldog whirled around.

John Bull had courage. On three legs he waddled toward Brownie. I heard Uncle Will say, "Use that on the dog and

I'll use this on you." I looked up and saw Harkess put his gun back in his holster. Uncle Will kept his in his hand.

This time Brownie jumped for John Bull. They made so much dust you couldn't see what was happening. Again I heard the crunching sound and saw Brownie jump back. John Bull with both hind legs broken now dragged himself toward Brownie on his two front paws.

Harkess started toward his dog. I heard a shot and saw a puff of dust kick up at the saloon keeper's feet. Uncle Will said, "You try to stop this fight and I'll kill you."

"But John Bull is worth a thousand dollars," Harkess pleaded. "Maybe if I get him to a vet I can save him."

Uncle Will shook his head. "You never worried about saving any of the dogs that John Bull killed. I am not about to start worrying about your dog."

I had to admire John Bull. He never barked or made a sound, just kept lunging toward Brownie. My dog circled John Bull until he got the bulldog's head half turned, then leaped and grabbed John Bull's front leg. They rolled in the dust and I heard the crunching sound again. Brownie jumped back.

I thought it was all over until I heard a man say, "John Bull will still kill him if he gets hold of that other dog's throat."

I saw the prediction almost come true. Brownie leaped for the remaining front leg and missed it. John Bull grabbed Brownie's throat. They rolled and thumped in the dust. I began to cry. Then I jumped and clapped my hands. Brownie had broken away. The blood John Bull had lost, and his three smashed legs, had weakened him so that he couldn't keep his hold. Brownie sank his teeth into John Bull's throat.

John Bull's fighting spirit did not yield for almost five

minutes; then his body shuddered and lay still. Brownie released his grip and backed away. He watched John Bull for a moment, then walked over and nudged the bulldog with his nose. Forgetting all about his snobbish decorum he gave a loud bark of joy and ran into my waiting arms.

22

THE PASSING OF THE
LAREDO KID

IF WE CHILDREN thought that we were through with the Catechism lessons after Aunt Cathie left, we soon found we were mistaken. Mamma began teaching us, struggling to understand and interpret the tenets of the Catholic religion. She spent hours with Papa asking him for explanations and help. Even Tom, who was going to be a Mormon, didn't mind studying with us, because with his great brain he had to know everything.

Papa drove us over to Castle Rock for Mass at least once a month. Then one day Mamma told us that Aunt Cathie was coming back.

"Shucks," Tom said in disgust, "that means no more laughing in this house and Grandpa and Grandma Neilsen won't come to visit us any more."

"Do not use the word 'shucks,'" Mamma reprimanded him. "And I'm certain we all will find Aunt Cathie an entirely different person. Her prayers and God have made her so, or she wouldn't return."

My memory of Aunt Cathie's return is always associated with the Laredo Kid, a gunman with a bad reputation. They both arrived on the same day. His first night in town the

Laredo Kid killed a man named Bartlett during an argument over a card game in the Allies Saloon. The next day he goaded a sheepherder into going for his gun, and killed the man.

Papa went to see Marshal Gentry. "You must run that Laredo Kid out of town, Hal. The Saints won't stand for these killings and turning East Adenville into a hangout for gunmen."

"What can I do?" the Marshal asked. "Both men went for their guns."

"It was murder just the same," Papa told him.

"All right, Tom," Gentry said. "I'll run the Laredo Kid out of town."

That afternoon Marshal Gentry went into the Allies Saloon and gave the Laredo Kid until sundown to leave.

Just before the sun set behind the mountain range, Marshal Gentry was in the Whitehorse Saloon talking to Uncle Will.

"You sure you can handle him, Hal?" Uncle Will asked.

"I'm a little rusty," the Marshal admitted, "but I can take care of him."

Windy Davis burst through the swinging doors. "The Laredo Kid is on his way here, Hal. He's been bragging you wouldn't have to come looking for him."

Marshal Gentry checked his guns and walked outside, where he stood in the middle of the street waiting for the Laredo Kid to come within pistol range. Uncle Will and a crowd had gathered on the wooden sidewalk in front of the Whitehorse Saloon.

The Laredo Kid slowed his steps as he approached to within shooting distance. "It's sundown, Marshal," he shouted, "and I'm still here."

In his prime Marshal Gentry could have easily killed the

Laredo Kid; but time had taken its toll of his reflexes. He'd just managed to get his gun from the holster when the Laredo Kid's gun blazed. The first bullet caught Gentry in the chest, and the next one in the head.

Uncle Will rushed to the street. After making certain Gentry was dead, he faced the Laredo Kid, who had holstered his guns.

"He was my friend, damn you!"

The Laredo Kid exuded confidence. "Just line up, boys," he said sneeringly. "I'm willing to accommodate all the Marshal's friends."

Uncle Will removed his frock coat. His jeweled holster gleamed in the fading light. "Hit leather first," Uncle Will challenged, "I never take favors."

The hands of both men were blurred as they drew. Two shots rang out. Uncle Will grabbed his stomach and pitched forward on his face. His shot had gone wild. He had been hit first.

The Laredo Kid looked at the crowd. "All right, boys, who's next?" When nobody moved, he turned his back and strode toward the Allies Saloon.

Windy Davis brought Papa the news. We were eating supper, and although it was too early to tell, it seemed to me that Aunt Cathie had changed a lot. Papa went to the front door. When he came back his face was white.

"The Laredo Kid just killed Hal Gentry and seriously wounded Will," Papa said hoarsely. He went into the hallway and removed a holster and gun from the gun rack.

For the first time I saw Mamma hysterical. She jumped up from the table and threw her arms around Papa's neck. "What can you do? You— You— Oh dear God, you can't be thinking of— No, no, Tom dear."

Papa took Mamma's wrists and disengaged her arms. "I'm sorry, Tena girl, but there is no other way."

"But, Tom," Mamma cried as she struggled to free her wrists from his grasp, "my dearest husband, I won't let you. You must think of me and the children."

Papa nodded slowly. "I am thinking of you and the children, Tena girl. What child could honor and love a father who was lacking in honor and love himself? I do what I do because I must. You know, my dear, that if I shirked my duty in this, you could no longer respect me. It is far better to die with honor than to live in dishonor. When I adopted the West as my home, I also adopted its customs and codes. I'm going, Tena girl, with or without your consent."

Mamma suddenly became composed. She raised herself on her tiptoes and kissed Papa. "I understand, Tom dear. I shall not try to dissuade you with tears. God bless you and protect you."

Papa looked around the table and without another word strode from the house. Aunt Bertha and Aunt Cathie sat as if stunned. For the first time in my life I was too frightened to cry. Mamma went into the parlor and we all followed her. She knelt and began to pray. We prayed with her. She got up and went to the piano. She began to play and sing a hymn. I remember it was "Love at Home." We crowded around her. One by one we began singing, all except Aunt Cathie.

As Papa walked toward the Allies Saloon, Uncle Mark entered it. He stopped just inside the door until his eyes found the Laredo Kid leaning against the bar talking to Harkess. Uncle Mark walked toward the bar. He stopped about ten feet from the Laredo Kid. Patrons scrambled to get out of the line of fire.

The Laredo Kid turned slowly around, keeping his elbows on the bar as he leaned back against it and faced Uncle Mark. "Is this another of the Marshal's friends?" he jeered as he looked around at the crowd.

Uncle Mark stood with his thumb hooked carelessly in the belt of his holster. "Marshal Gentry gave you until sundown to leave town," he said. "I'm the Marshal of West Adenville. With Gentry dead, I am now the Marshal of East Adenville as well. Go for your gun, or I'll kill you in cold blood."

There were witnesses who swore that Uncle Mark didn't move a muscle until the Laredo Kid's gun was half out of its holster, then with a motion so fast the eye couldn't follow it, he drew. A single shot rang out. The bullet caught the Laredo Kid in the face and plowed upward through his brain, killing him instantly.

Uncle Mark put his gun back in his holster. He looked at Dan Harkess. "He was your friend, Harkess. You hired him to come here and kill Will Fitzgerald just to get even for that damn dog of yours. Go for your gun, Harkess, or I'll take you down to the boys at the Whitehorse Saloon and let them hang you. Draw, damn you!"

At this moment Papa entered the saloon. Papa ran to Uncle Mark and grabbed him by the shoulder. "Wait, Mark!"

Dan Harkess took advantage of this interruption to reach for his gun. Uncle Mark shoved Papa aside and beat Harkess to the draw by a split second. Harkess slumped to the floor dead.

Uncle Mark holstered his gun. "With Marshal Gentry's death, I am the law around here."

He turned and walked from the saloon with Papa. When they reached the street, Mark said: "I had to do it, Tom.

When you are dealing with skunks you've got to talk their own language."

Papa shook his head. "I know why you did this, Mark. And once again, as has happened during every crisis in my life, I'm indebted to you. I know you didn't want to kill Harkess. I know the only reason you did was you knew he'd kill me later, or hire another gunman to do it. Words are meaningless at a time like this. How do you thank a man for your life?"

Uncle Mark shrugged. "Forget it, Tom. And if you value my friendship, I'd rather Tena never knew the real reason. I want her to think I killed both men doing my duty as a Marshal."

But Mamma knew, because many years later she told me how Uncle Mark had hurried to the Allies Saloon to get there before Papa did.

23

THE SALVATION OF
UNCLE WILL

GIVEN A CROSS TO BEAR, some men find strength through prayer, some through loved ones, some through work; wise men become philosophers. A few men, like Uncle Will, attempt to shift the weight of the cross from their own shoulders to those of their loved ones. When Dr. LeRoy told my uncle that the bullet from the Laredo Kid's gun had lodged in his spine in such a manner as to paralyze my uncle from the hips down, Uncle Will cursed the doctor for being a bungling incompetent. It wasn't until Aunt Queenie had taken him to Denver, and from there to Boston, where specialists told my uncle he would never walk again, that Uncle Will believed the diagnosis.

The day Uncle Will arrived back home from Boston, Papa boarded the train and carried Uncle Will in his arms to the wheel chair on the platform. We children crowded around him and tried to kiss him, but he pushed us away. I saw him grit his teeth when Mamma kissed him. As Papa put his hands on the rail of the wheel chair, Uncle Will shouted, "Take your damn hands off that. I'll push myself right up Main Street."

The Uncle Will we all knew died when he became a cripple. He had grown quarrelsome, bitter, cynical, and he showed small appreciation for the care and affection his wife and others lavished upon him. He was drunk all the time, and when Mamma remonstrated with Aunt Queenie for giving him all the whiskey he wanted to drink, Aunt Queenie said, "It helps him to forget for a little while."

The townspeople got used to seeing Uncle Will drunk in his wheel chair on the front porch of his home. They endured the way he would shout at little children. "Run, skip and jump, you lucky little devils, while you can." Sometimes he shouted at adults walking by: "Walk up and down in front of me, damn you. Let me know you got legs and I haven't."

His best friends, Judge Baker and Dandy Allen, tried to persuade him that he could still go to the Whitehorse Saloon and run the big stake poker table. "Get out, damn you," Uncle Will shouted at them. "You want people to look at me and pity me? Get out, damn you!"

When Aunt Cathie returned, she told Papa she wanted to live alone and find some type of work to support herself. Papa bought her a small house and had the parlor in it fixed up as a millinery shop. The house was half a block from Uncle Will's. As time passed Aunt Cathie and Aunt Queenie became the best of friends.

Aunt Cathie visited them often. When she tried to get Uncle Will to let her read from her prayer book to him, he shouted, "I'll die as I lived, an agnostic." Aunt Cathie brought Father Caffarella over from Castle Rock to see Uncle Will, but he ordered the priest out of his house.

The first time he threatened to kill himself, Aunt Queenie took all the shells for his guns and hid them. He talked so irrationally that she later became so worried she threw away his razor and had the barber come to the house to shave him. He'd get drunk and throw the whiskey bottle against the wall. "Give me a gun," he'd scream. "If you love me, give me a gun. Let me blow my damn brains out. I'd rather be dead than a half a man like I am now."

He was almost as bad with Papa. Once he said, "If you loved me like a brother, you'd give me a gun. If you loved me as much as an animal, you'd give me a gun. A horse breaks its leg and you shoot it to put it out of its misery. But a man, no. You in your damn ignorant, superstitious religious belief won't give me the same consideration you'd give a horse. Now I can feel some of the hell that Doc Tethers went through."

One day, almost two years after Uncle Will became a cripple, Windy Davis showed up at the Whitehorse Saloon with money. Windy was not only buying his own drinks but drinks for others. Dandy Allen and Judge Baker took Windy into a back room. Dandy, who was running the saloon now, threw Windy into a chair.

"Where did you get the money, Windy?" he demanded.

"I won it in a card game," Windy replied.

Dandy slapped Davis across the mouth. "You're lying, Windy. Now talk, you drunken fool, or I'll beat you until you do."

Windy dropped his head in his hands. "He was my friend," he sobbed. "My best friend. Windy, he sez, I've never axed you for a favor in return for all the favors I did you. Windy, he sez, they got it fixed at the store so I can't buy any shells for my gun. Windy, he sez, here's a hundred dollars if you'll get me some shells. I done it. I couldn't help it. It ain't right for a man like him to be sittin' there a cripple."

Dandy Allen ran all the way to Uncle Will's house. He

found Aunt Queenie in the backyard hanging up clothes. "Where's Will?" he asked.

Queenie looked surprised. "Isn't he sitting on the lawn in front?"

Allen shook his head and told her what had happened. "Don't worry, we'll find him."

"Wait," Aunt Queenie said as she unwrapped the cloth tied around her head, shaking her copper-colored hair loose. "Never mind looking for him, Dandy. I know where to find him. You and Judge Baker come for us and bring a buckboard with you in about an hour. We'll be waiting for you at the old Whitehorse Saloon in Silverlode."

Dandy nodded slowly. "I've said a million times you are a thoroughbred, Queenie. There have been times when I hated Will, but more times when I loved him like a brother. I can't say I wouldn't have done what Windy did if Will had asked me."

Uncle Will had pushed his wheel chair across the bridge over Aden Ditch. The road over the plateau wasn't used any more except for logging, and rains had cut big gulleys in it. Falling boulders made the going in the wheel chair very hard. When he'd gone far enough up Whiskey Row to see the old Whitehorse Saloon, Uncle Will found the road blocked by a big rock. There were holes on both sides of it. He knew he couldn't get around it. He shook his fist at the rock and begun to curse.

Suddenly he felt someone pushing the wheel chair. He grabbed the wheels and stopped it. He looked over his shoulder at his wife. He pulled a loaded revolver from beneath the blanket that covered his useless legs. "Try turning this damn thing around and I'll blow my brains out right in front of you," he screamed.

She smiled through her tears. "No, honey, you aren't going back. If I help you, we can get around that boulder."

Uncle Will was suspicious. "Nothing you can say will make me change my mind. I'm tired of living in this damn thing."

"I'm not going to say anything or do anything to try and stop you, honey. I knew this is where you'd want it to end. I only came to help you get to the old Whitehorse. I told Dandy and Judge Baker to come for us in an hour."

As she helped him get the chair around the boulder and they neared the old Whitehorse Saloon, he became very calm. "Can you understand why it had to be here, Queenie? I was a man's man in those days. There wasn't a man in the Territory I couldn't lick with my fists. There wasn't a gun slinger in the Territory I couldn't beat to the draw. There wasn't a gambler in the Territory I couldn't beat at poker without cheating. I owned the biggest and best damn saloon and gambling hall in the Territory. I was a king. I even had my court—men like Hal Gentry, Dandy Allen, Dave Powell —and even a court jester in Windy Davis. I was a man's man in those days."

Aunt Queenie whispered, "I remember. I remember."

They stopped at the intersection of what had once been Whiskey Row and Corry Street. Uncle Will looked up at what remained of the Whitehorse Saloon. "I never rightly knew why I didn't sell the lumber in it to the Mormons and let them tear it down. It was a premonition, I guess. I knew that some day I'd return and when I did, I wanted it to be standing here."

The sign with the white horse on it had been blown down and lay on the ground. The wooden sidewalk had long since been torn up and taken away by the thrifty Saints. The boards of the old building were buckled and warped from the weather; their white paint had long since blistered and peeled off.

Aunt Queenie pushed the wheel chair near the swinging doors, one of which was hanging on a single hinge. With the wooden sidewalk gone, it was almost three feet to the doorway from the ground. Uncle Will put the gun in his jeweled holster. He set his hands and tried to pull himself up and through the doorway, but his hands slipped and he fell back in the chair.

Aunt Queenie began to cry.

"Don't try to help me," Uncle Will said. "I've got to get inside and I want to do it on my own power." He got another grip on the doorway. With sweat breaking out on his forehead he pulled his body slowly upward, heaved himself inside the doorway on his face. "Bring the wheel chair," he called to Aunt Queenie as he pulled himself out of the doorway by walking on his hands and dragging his legs behind him.

Aunt Queenie lifted the wheel chair through the doorway. She climbed up herself and then helped Uncle Will into the chair. He leaned back and stared around the barren dusty room as birds took flight from it.

"Do you see what I see, Queenie?" he asked, his voice shaking with emotion. "I see all the ghosts of Silverlode. I see myself entering the Whitehorse for the first time. There was something about it that made me want to own it. I'd never wanted to own anything before. I'd heard how Nat Breen had killed two men who won the place from him in poker games. I knew if I could get him into a game and make him lose enough, I could win the Whitehorse from him. I knew I'd have to kill him when the game was over. I was ready for him when he went for his gun."

Aunt Queenie knelt in the dust on the floor and placed

her head in his lap. "I remember, Will. I remember the
first time I saw you. I was coming down the stairs and my
eyes seemed to fasten upon you at once. I couldn't stop
looking at you all night. I remember saying to myself that
if I could get a man like you, I'd never want another thing
from life. I was probably the only person here that night
who knew you would be more than a match for Nat Breen
at cards and with a gun. And when you picked me for your
girl, I was never more happy in my life."

He began to caress her hair. "I never told you, Queenie,
but you were the first woman with whom I'd ever spent
more than a single night. During all those years when I was
a king, I never told you once that I loved you, and yet you
must have known."

"Yes, honey, I knew," she said kissing his hand. "A woman
always knows when a man really loves her. And when you
made me your wife, I prayed that night for the first time
since I was a child. I thanked God for letting me love you
and be loved in return. I promised God that I would love
you in life and in death."

"Thank you, dear," he said. "But I shall die as I have
lived believing that all religions are fairy tales told by the
weak to enslave the strong."

She looked up at him. "It may seem strange for you to
think of me being religious after the life I've lived. When
Cathie became such a a good friend and I confessed to her
how little I knew of religion, she began teaching me Catholicism. I needed something to give me the strength to bear
the pain I felt every time I looked at you in that wheel chair.
The day Father Caffarella came to see you, I told him I
wanted to become a Catholic. I had found the strength
through faith to bear the ache in my heart because you were
a cripple."

Uncle Will shook his head. "Religion is a strange thing. If you believe a thing to be true, then to you it is true."

She smiled at him. "I have always believed in God because I feared Him, until Tena taught me that God is love. I feel very close to God right now. Religion tells us that what we are about to do is a sin, but—"

He cupped her chin in his hand and lifted her face. "What do you mean when you say what we are about to do?"

She pressed the palm of his hand to her lips. "You didn't think I would let you die alone did you, sweetheart? I've lived only to be near you and love you. Without you life would be like this building, with nothing but haunting memories. I am not afraid to die. Tena says that God is love, and if God is love, then He must understand that what we do, we do only because we are so very much in love."

Uncle Will bent over and kissed her. "No hysterics, no pleading, just the woman I love right down to the last chip in the game. I understand how you feel. I felt that way when you were so ill and I thought you were going to die. I was terrified at the thought of living without you. If I loved you less, I could not do this."

He removed the gun from its holster. He cast one last look around the deserted saloon. For one precious moment they were all there—Barnaby Smith with his derby hat on the back of his head at the piano, Horseshoe Jim with his gleaming stickpin and his toupee pushed to the back of his head, Doc Tethers getting drunk at the bar with the hunchback called Peter standing in back of him, Dave Powell mincing his way on his small feet toward the bar, Hal Gentry at a table polishing his gun with a chamois, Judge Baker holding forth in a political argument with a drink in one hand while he rubbed his porous red nose with the other,

Dandy Allen with his amethyst cuff links glistening as he dealt cards at the big stake poker table, Windy Davis with his bleary eyes roving around looking for a winner so he could cadge a chip to buy a drink, Butch Mears knocking the heads of two miners together during a drunken quarrel, and Queenie in a green velvet dress with her hand on his shoulder as he played poker.

A clap of thunder shook the building. A flash of lightning followed, and then the sound of rain beating on the roof.

Queenie got to her feet. She leaned over and kissed him. "They will be coming soon, sweetheart. I'm going to say I love you because they are the last words I want to speak. I am ready, sweetheart. I love you."

Straight as a poplar tree she stood without a tremor in her body. Her eyes were radiant and there was a gentle smile on her lips.

Slowly Uncle Will raised his pearl-handled revolver and pointed it at her heart. "Goodbye, my dear," he whispered. "There was never a woman like you. I love you." The hammer of the gun clicked as it struck the cap of the cartridge.

Uncle Will stared at the gun for a moment and then broke it open. He examined the markings made by the hammer of the gun striking the shell. He replaced the shell in the gun so the same shell would be in position to fire. He pointed the gun toward where the bar of the saloon had once been. He pulled the trigger. There was a deafening explosion that shook the building. Uncle Will leaned back in the wheel chair. The gun dangled from his fingers for a moment and then dropped to the floor. He bent forward and dropped his face in his hands. "I can't fight odds like that," he cried out as he felt his head being cradled in the arms of his wife.

When Dandy Allen and Judge Baker reached the old

Whitehorse Saloon, they saw Uncle Will sitting in the wheel chair in the doorway with Queenie standing beside him. The mountain shower had ended and a rainbow was arched over the canyon.

Uncle Will laughed, "Well, don't just sit there, boys. Put me in the buckboard. Don't be afraid, I'm not a ghost. We've slain the last ghost of Silverlode. And Dandy, the first thing in the morning, tell all the boys I'll be back at the Whitehorse tomorrow."

The following Saturday Uncle Will drove to Castle Rock with Aunt Queenie and Aunt Cathie. They went to Confession that night and remained overnight at a hotel so they could go to early Mass and Communion in the morning.

After my Uncle Will had returned to his faith he became one of the gentlest and most cheerful of men.

24

LOVE COMES TO AUNT CATHIE

W<small>HEN</small> <small>AUNT</small> <small>CATHIE</small> opened her millinery shop in West Adenville, the only business she got was from the dance hall girls in East Adenville and the wives of the mining officials at Castle Rock. She came to our house for dinner almost every Sunday. In time, with Mamma's and Uncle Mark's help, some of the Mormon women began to patronize Aunt Cathie's shop.

Uncle Mark was Aunt Cathie's constant companion. When they eloped to Salt Lake City, where they were married in a civil ceremony, only Mamma knew they were going. Aunt Cathie came to see Mamma the day before the elopement. In the privacy of Mamma's bedroom she bared her soul. "Tena dear, I need your strength, your wisdom, your counsel. I have been in love with Mark for a long time, but refused to admit it even to myself. I keep telling myself that it cannot be. I tell myself that he has killed men."

"But Cathie," Mamma interrupted, "Mark is an officer of the law. I know you are referring to the time Mark killed the Laredo Kid and Dan Harkess, but do you know why he killed them, Cathie? I shall tell you. You know that my husband was on his way to the Allies Saloon that night. You also know that Tom never would have had a chance against that gunman. Well, Mark knew it too. That was why he hurried to the saloon ahead of Tom. That was why he killed both men. He did it to save your brother's life."

"Thank you, Tena," Cathie said. "Even as I told myself he had killed men, I walked with him and dogs barked joyously when they saw him. Children ran after him just to have him speak to them and pat them on the head. But that isn't all, Tena. I've begged Mark to become a Catholic. But he is the most honorable of men. He said that he couldn't justify his conscience if he did. God help me, Tena," Aunt Cathie began to cry, "I'd love him no matter what manner of man he was or what his religion might be. I love him so much I cannot escape from him even through prayer. I must marry him or enter a convent. Tell me, Tena, when you faced almost the same decision before you married my brother where, oh where, did you get the strength to do it?"

"From my love for Tom," Mamma answered. "If you think of God as religion, Cathie, then you must not marry Mark. If you think of God as love, then you should marry Mark. I find nowhere in any Christian religion a commandment that God has forbidden those of one religious faith to marry those of another faith. You must know, Cathie, that God in His infinite wisdom could not be so intolerant. Marry Mark, Cathie. Marry Mark and you will find great happiness. Believe me, Cathie, you need not be afraid."

Aunt Cathie stood up. A smile of rapture spread over her delicate features. "Thank you, Tena, my dear. I came to you pleading for some of your strength to give me the courage to do what my heart tells me to do, and I found it. But the decision shall be my very own. I want it to be my own.

I shall say it for the first time. I love Mark Trainor and I am going to marry him."

The change in Aunt Cathie when she returned from the Retreat and the months she'd spent in meditation had been almost miraculous. It seemed that she was always trying to be more and more like Mamma. When she and Uncle Mark returned from their honeymoon she had changed even more. She was bubbling over with happiness all the time. She joined the women's clubs and in no time at all was calling almost everyone in town by his first name. She visited Mormon women in their homes and invited them into hers. She was very proud of the house Uncle Mark built for her near Uncle Will's and Aunt Queenie's.

Then gradually the trips Aunt Cathie took with Papa, Katie, Sweyn, Earnie and me to St. Joseph's in Castle Rock became fewer and fewer. Mormon Ward teachers began calling on Aunt Cathie, and Bishop Aden visited her several times.

When she was pregnant with her first child she called a meeting of the family in our house. Grandpa and Grandma Neilsen drove over from Enoch with Mark's father, Bishop Trainor. Papa, Mamma, Aunt Bertha' (who was practically a member of the family), Uncle Will and Aunt Queenie were there.

Aunt Cathie sat with Uncle Mark standing beside her and holding her hand. "God has blessed me with a happiness I didn't think existed on this earth," she said quietly. "To-morrow I shall accompany Mark and his father to Enoch. There, Bishop Trainor will baptize and confirm me in the faith of my husband." She looked at Papa and Uncle Will. "I want you, my dear brothers, to know that not one Saint said a word to convert me that I did not ask them to say. Once the veil of religious bigotry was lifted from my eyes, I saw the truth in Mormonism and the simple, sweet goodness of the Latter-Day Saints. I have known for a long time that Mark has yearned to return to his faith. When I became pregnant, I suddenly knew that I wanted our child, and any other child God may bless us with, to grow up in the faith of their father." She looked at Mamma and smiled. "For God is love and not a religion. My brother, Father John, often said that all religions are but windows in the same church letting in the light of God. I shall joyfully embrace my husband's religion and later be sealed in marriage to him in the St. George or Salt Lake Temple."

Grandpa Neilsen leaned on his gold-handled umbrella which he now used as a cane. "We walk different roads. We sing different hymns. We say different prayers. We build churches of different architecture. And yet we all have the same goal, the Kingdom of Heaven."

25

REQUIEM

THE CRISES in our family were now all resolved. We settled down to enjoy golden years. Aunt Cathie had two more children. Sweyn left home to attend All Hallows College in Salt Lake City. A year later Earnie left for the same Catholic boarding school, and Katie went to St. Mary's Academy in the same city.

It was very lonely for me the following year when Tom left for Brigham Young Academy at Provo. The year after, I joined Sweyn and Earnie at All Hallows, and Mamma and Papa were left with an empty house.

When Sweyn graduated, Papa, Mamma, Grandpa and Grandma Neilsen, Aunt Cathie and Queenie, Uncle Will and Uncle Mark all came to Salt Lake City for one glorious week. Papa took us all to the Salt Lake Theater where the costumes and scenery enthralled me. Grandpa took me through the Tabernacle, with its ten-foot-thick arches making a span of one hundred and fifty feet, and seventy feet high in the center; and he told me the timbers were fastened with wooden dowel pins and rawhide throngs. I could not go into the Temple because only Latter-Day Saints are permitted to enter it; but Grandpa told me how it took forty

[284]

years to complete it. I remember Papa, Sweyn, Earnie, Uncle Will, Aunt Queenie and I going to Mass at the Cathedral of the Madeleine while Mamma, Grandpa and Grandma Neilsen, my brother Tom, Aunt Cathie and Uncle Mark went to church at the Tabernacle.

When we returned to West Adenville we had dinner at our house. Later in the parlor with the whole family present Grandpa Neilsen leaned on his cane and looked at Papa. "I know you cannot afford to educate all your sons and Earnest," he said. "We are a family. Sweyn Dennis has told me he has decided upon a career. He wants to be a doctor. I shall defray his entire expenses to send him East to a medical school."

Mamma smiled. "Sweyn D. would make a good doctor. He was always bringing home birds with broken wings and other animals that had been hurt."

Grandpa spoke bluntly to Papa. "I know what a poor businessman you are, Tom. I know of the countless men you have grubstaked. I know of your foolish investments in mining stocks. You had numerous opportunities to become a wealthy man but failed to take advantage of them. I can temper this criticism by saying that in a way I am glad. Life is the pursuit of happiness and not of wealth."

Grandpa turned to Uncle Will. "You are a wealthy man. When Earnest graduates from school next year why not send him to an art school back East? If his talent is proven to be as good as I believe it to be, perhaps you might even send him to Paris."

Uncle Will rubbed a finger across his graying mustache. "I have told Tom a dozen times I would gladly pay for the education of all the children."

Grandpa Neilsen shook his head. "No. We are a family." Then he looked at my brother Tom. "Now we come to the

Mormon in the family," he smiled. "The Patriarch's Blessing said that one child would heal the sick, one would bring beauty to the world and one would spread the gospel of the Prophet, Joseph Smith. Tom Dennis will graduate from Brigham Young Academy next year. He tells me that his greatest desire is to go on a mission. Bishop Aden will call Tom Dennis on a mission to the Orient for three years as soon as the boy graduates. Mormon missionaries travel without purse or script. There is only the passage money to consider. We will work that out when the time comes."

Tom had never deviated from his desire to be a Mormon, but this was the first time I knew anything about him going on a mission. I didn't have a doubt that with Tom's great brain, he'd make Saints out of those millions of Chinese in jig time.

Grandpa Sweyn looked at me. "It is good for any family if one son follows in the footsteps of his father. You won't graduate from All Hallows for two years. You must start thinking about what you want to be in life, John."

Katie felt left out. She walked over to Grandpa. "What about me, Grandpa?"

Mamma spoke up. "I think your career is settled. You will marry Felix Dussiere."

Katie tossed her head. "I don't know if I'll marry Felix or not. I haven't exactly promised him I would."

Grandpa smiled at her. "You have quite a few years to think it over, young lady."

It was a wonderful summer with all of us home.

Sweyn left for Baltimore to study medicine the year Reed Smoot began his four-year fight for his seat in Congress.

Tom left on his mission to the Orient right after the completion of the San Pedro, Los Angeles and Salt Lake Railroad, which brought Utah into direct rail communication with Southern California.

Earnie went to New York to study art the year of the San Francisco earthquake.

My sister Katie was married to Felix Dussiere in St. Joseph's in Castle Rock the year I graduated from All Hallows College. They went to live on the big Dussiere Ranch.

I didn't know Papa was ill until the fall of that year. I noticed he looked a little thinner but his appetite and disposition always seemed good. One afternoon while Papa was at *The Advocate* Mamma called me into the parlor. I could see she'd been crying. I dropped to my knees in front of her rocker. "Mamma, why are you crying?"

She looked at me. "John D., would you mind very much if you didn't get to go to college this year."

"Is that all?" I felt relieved. "Of course I don't mind. If there isn't enough money, I can work for a year and save some."

She brushed my hair back with her hand. "It isn't the money, son. Your Uncle Will would gladly give you the money. It's Papa. He is very ill. All the children are away from home now, except you. I want you to stay home. I want you to go to *The Advocate* with Papa every day and help him. You must promise that you will never speak of his illness to him."

"But Mamma," I cried, "you must tell me what it is. Can't the doctor do anything for Papa?"

"While you were at school, John D., Doctor LeRoy and I took Papa to a specialist in Salt Lake. The specialist confirmed what Doctor LeRoy had feared. Papa has cancer. At first Doctor LeRoy thought it might be due to consumption, but the tests taken showed this wasn't the reason. There is no other explanation for the loss in weight."

"Oh my God," I cried. "How long—how long before—"

"We don't know," Mamma said as she wiped the tears from her eyes. "That is why it is such a cruel disease. It may be a few months. It may be a year or more. Now, John D., you must promise me that you will never pity Papa. You must pretend that everything is just as it always was. You must tell him that you don't want to leave me alone and will wait until Tom D. returns from his mission before you go to college."

"I promise, Mamma," I said. "Are you sure, Mamma, that Papa isn't suffering from pain?"

Mamma shook her head sadly. "That we will never really know. Papa, being Papa, would conceal from us any suffering he may endure, because he knows it would hurt us."

I did not have to ask Papa whether I might stay home. He must have wanted to make certain one of us boys was home to comfort Mamma in case he died. "J. D.," he said to me a few days after I had talked with Mamma, "I hate to let you down like this, but there just isn't enough money to send you to school. Would you feel terribly disappointed if you had to postpone your education for another year?" It was the only time Papa ever lied to me.

"Of course not, Papa," I answered. "And the year won't be wasted because I'm going to spend every day of it at *The Advocate* with you. I want to be a journalist and instead of serving my apprenticeship after I get out of college, I'll serve it now, under you."

Papa went right on living as if nothing were the matter with him. He drank his usual glass of brandy after supper and smoked his usual cigar. He put in the same hours at *The Advocate*. He invited sheepmen, cattlemen and other people to Sunday dinners. He taught me how to set type and run the presses. He permitted me to do the make-ready for the handbills. He told me the history of journalism and the fourth estate. He encouraged me to read all the newspapers he received with their diametrically opposed editorial policies on religion, events and politics. During that year he instilled within me as much of his own philosophy of life as he could.

The next summer Sweyn remained in Baltimore to serve part of his internship. Earnie was in New York. Katie at the Dussiere Ranch was pregnant. Tom was on his way home from his mission to the Orient.

The day Grandpa and Grandma Neilsen arrived, it was raining. It rained for seven days straight. Katie and her husband were staying at our house because she wanted to be with Mamma when the baby was born. My brother Tom was due to arrive the next day. I thought that was the reason Grandpa and Grandma had come.

The Latter-Day Saints believe in Revelation. They believed in those days that the devout among them were gifted with the power to have revelations of future events in their lives or events which would affect the history of their religion. That night Grandpa called Mamma into the kitchen. "My daughter," he said as he leaned on his umbrella which he now used for a cane, "I had a revelation some time ago that when Tom Dennis returned from his mission his father would die. The same revelation came to me three times. I sent telegrams to Sweyn and Earnest to come home. They should arrive within a day or two after Tom Dennis. You must be brave, daughter."

Mamma placed her arms around Grandpa. "If it be God's will to take my beloved husband, I shall thank God for ending the terrible suffering Tom is enduring. He never complains; but the doctor told me that even the pills and medicine he gives Tom cannot give him more than a temporary relief. I shall also thank God for letting me share these many years with such a kind, generous and devoted husband."

I watched Papa carefully the next day at *The Advocate*. He seemed more cheerful than he'd ever been. I supposed it was because he knew Tom, Earnie and Sweyn were on their way home.

I remember how gay and happy Papa was the night the whole family once again sat down for supper. Besides us children and Katie's husband Felix Dussiere, there were Uncle Will, Uncle Mark, Aunt Queenie, Aunt Cathie and her children, Grandpa and Grandma Neilsen, Aunt Bertha, Bishop Aden and his daughter Julia (whom Tom was to marry one day), and Mamma—all seated around the table. Papa always let Grandpa ask the blessing when he was staying at our house, but this night, Papa asked Grandpa if he might ask it.

"Oh Lord, I thank Thee for Thy many blessings. I thank Thee for graciously permitting me to be gathered to the bosom of my family and my dearest friend. Bless the food we eat. Bless this house. Bless each and every one of us. In the name of the Saviour, Jesus Christ. Amen."

We all crowded into the parlor after supper and Tom kept us enthralled as he told of his experiences on the mission.

The next morning I went to *The Advocate* as usual with Papa. About mid-morning as I was setting type for a handbill of a livestock auction, Papa pressed his hand against his stomach and swayed on his feet. I dropped the type to the floor and ran to him. After helping him to a chair, I got two pills from the prescription bottle in his desk and gave them to him. He took a deep breath, shook his head, and then began methodically to pull papers from the pigeonholes in his desk, scrutinizing each one. Some he threw into the waste basket, others he replaced in the pigeonholes. When he had finished, he got up and removed his green eyeshade, walked over to the press and gently patted it. He asked me to help him on with his coat. I put on my own and got the umbrella because it was still raining. Papa took one last look around the office, then turned to me. "Take me home, now, J. D."

He insisted on walking home instead of letting me go for a buggy. His eyes seemed to be saying a personal good-bye to every tree and building along the street.

When we entered our parlor, Mamma came in from the kitchen with flour from kneading bread on her hands and arms. "Tena girl," Papa said simply, "I want to go to bed."

Dr. LeRoy came several times during the next three days, and either Mamma, Mrs. Miller or Aunt Bertha was with Papa every moment. On the third day Father Caffarella came, and remained with Papa all through the day and into the night. Mamma came out of the bedroom very late the night of that third day.

"Papa is dying," Mamma said softly. "He wants to be married in the Catholic faith and to live long enough to see his grandchild. I ask you to pray to God to spare Papa until his two wishes are granted." We all knelt while Father Caffarella heard Papa's last confession and gave him extreme unction.

Meanwhile Dr. LeRoy had gone upstairs to see how my sister was.

Father Caffarella came out of the bedroom, and we heard Papa call: "Tena girl, get my clothes. I want to die with my boots on."

Uncle Mark helped Mamma get Papa dressed. Dr. LeRoy was still upstairs. Katie's husband Felix, who had been sitting in the kitchen, came running into the parlor. "Mrs. Miller says the baby is coming. The baby is coming." He looked around the room as if frightened and ran back to the kitchen.

Papa insisted that nobody help him walk from the bedroom into the parlor. He looked handsome even with the pallor of death on his cheeks. He sat down in his rocking chair just as the cry of a newborn baby was heard. Papa looked at Mamma and smiled. "If I might have a drink of brandy, Tena girl."

Mamma brought Papa the brandy and held the glass to his lips while he drank it. Aunt Bertha came downstairs and into the parlor. She shook her head with disbelief when she saw Papa. Then she cried out: "It's a boy. Mrs. Miller will bring him down as soon as Dr. LeRoy will let her."

Papa spoke to Father Caffarella, "God is good, Father. My grandson is born. May we have the services now?"

Mamma stood beside Papa's chair. Father Caffarella opened the missal he carried and began reading the marriage ritual. After the ceremony, Papa kissed Mamma and whispered, "Tena girl, my beloved wife and mother of my children."

This was the fourth time Papa and Mamma were married to each other.

Mrs. Miller came into the parlor carrying the baby. Felix followed her. Papa held the baby in his arms for a moment and then gave him back to Mrs. Miller. He motioned for Felix to come near him. He shook Felix by the hand. "Thank you for giving me a grandson. Now, please go to Katie and convey to her my gratitude and my dearest love."

After Mrs. Miller and Felix left, Papa asked for another drink of brandy. Mamma got it for him and held the glass to his lips. Then Papa leaned back in his chair. He looked at Grandpa and Grandma Neilsen. There were rasping noises in his throat as he spoke. "I could not love you both more if you were my own flesh and blood. I thank you for your understanding and your love. God bless you both."

He looked at Uncle Will and Aunt Cathie. "Never was a man blessed with a better brother and sister. I thank you for your love and affection." He looked at Aunt Queenie. "I thank you for loving my brother and bringing him back to the Church and breaking the curse of the lost one."

When Papa's dimming eyes looked at Uncle Mark he slowly shook his head. "There are no words, Mark, to express the depth of my love and affection for you. I could not love you more were you my own brother."

Papa smiled at Bishop Aden. "God was good to me when he permitted me to know you and become your friend. Your eyes are filled with tears for me. It is my eyes that should be filled with tears of gratitude for all you have done for me and my family. God bless you, old friend."

Then Papa called Sweyn, Earnie, Tom and me. As we knelt before him he placed his hands over our heads and asked God to bless us.

When the blessing was over, Papa took Mamma's hand and pressed it to his lips. "I shall love and cherish you after death as I have loved and cherished you in life, my dearest, Tena girl."

Then Papa asked for another glass of brandy. After drinking it, he tried to smoke a cigar but gave up after a few puffs.

"Father," he said to Father Caffarella, "I am ready to meet my God."

Then his mind began to ramble and he talked incoherently of many things. We would catch a word here and there as he continued his muttering for almost half an hour before Dr. LeRoy came into the parlor. He walked over and looked at Papa and felt his pulse. Then he looked at Mamma.

"He should be in bed," the doctor said sternly.

Mamma was quietly crying. "He wanted to die with his boots on."

Dr. LeRoy shook his head. "He doesn't know where he is now. Please let me put him to bed."

Mamma spoke to Papa. "Tom, dear, can you hear me?"

Papa just continued his muttering.

Mamma looked at the doctor. "We will lay him on the bed, but I will not permit you to undress him. He said he wanted to die with his boots on, and he shall."

Dr. LeRoy and Uncle Mark carried Papa into the bedroom.

Mamma sat at the bedside holding Papa's hand after he passed into a coma. When Dr. LeRoy begged her to lie down and get some rest, she said: "I must be with my husband. He knows I would not leave him alone."

All through the night the rain beat down, and the wind screamed against the house while Mamma held a rosary in Papa's hand. And the sky remained black as morning came. Dr. LeRoy came out of the bedroom and beckoned to Uncle Will, who pushed his wheel chair into the bedroom. Aunt Cathie followed Uncle Will into the bedroom. Then Father

Caffarella came from the bedroom and after making the sign of the Cross said softly, "God has taken him."

Bishop Aden talked for a long time to Father Caffarella in our parlor after Papa's death. Together they supervised the erection of a Catholic altar in the Latter-Day Saint Tabernacle, and the Mormons helped Father Caffarella bring all the things he needed from St. Joseph's in Castle Rock. The Latter-Day Saint choir practiced night and day until Papa's funeral to learn the Latin responses for the Mass, and the Ave Maria. Later Bishop Aden and the Reverend Holcomb came to our house and asked Mamma's and Father Caffarella's permission to kneel with us while the Rosary was said.

After the Mass for the Dead was said by Father Caffarella from the Catholic altar in the Mormon Tabernacle Bishop Aden couldn't finish the eulogy. I can almost repeat from memory the Bishop's words:

Brothers and sisters, we are gathered to mourn the passing of a great soul. I call you brothers and sisters whether you be Catholic, Protestant, Methodist, Mormon or Jew, because the man we mourn today was a brother to all faiths. He was a good man, a wise man, a just man, an honorable man, a kind man, a generous man and a devout man. He was a good father to his children and a devoted husband to his wife. He was every man's friend. He walked with God by his side every day of his life. There is not one amongst us who is not indebted to this good man in one way or another. His charity to men never robbed them of their dignity. This man did more to enable us of different faiths to live in harmony, tolerance and brotherly love than any other man I have ever known. In a tribute to the memory of Tom Fitzgerald we Saints want to donate the land upon which to build a Catholic church in West Adenville. We invite all who loved this man to contribute in materials and labor for this church. We—

At this point in his eulogy, Bishop Aden broke down and wept. "Forgive me, I loved him like a brother. God rest his noble soul. Amen."

After the funeral when the family was alone in our house, Grandpa Neilsen said to us children: "Each of you has inherited a grave responsibility. That responsibility is your father's good name. In anything you say and everything you do, you must ask yourself if your father would approve. Do this and you all shall be blessed with love and happiness."

The day Katie was well enough to come downstairs—she hadn't been able to attend the funeral—Mamma gathered all of us around her in the parlor. "Now we are alone," she said softly, "but we shall never know loneliness. We can borrow Papa back in our memories any time we feel lonely or need him. We can remember all the wonderful and joyous days we shared with him. We can recall the love, affection and understanding he gave us. We cannot help but grieve, but we will not carry our grief into our futures. Papa would not want that. Katie, as soon as you are stronger, you will return to the ranch with Felix."

"But, Mamma," Katie cried, "I can't bear to leave you alone."

"Your place is with your husband," Mamma said firmly. "Sweyn D. and Earnest D., you will return to school. Tom

D., you will take the position Bishop Aden obtained for you, and marry Julia. John D., you will go to school."

"But Mamma," I protested, "there isn't enough money."

"We will sell *The Advocate,*" Mamma answered.

Sweyn shook his head. "Papa wouldn't like that."

Mamma smiled at me. "I'm sorry, Sweyn D., but I don't believe John D. is ready to step into Papa's shoes. I have already spoken to Bishop Aden about it. He will find a buyer for the newspaper. Later, John D., after you've completed your education, if you choose to become a journalist like Papa, you can borrow the money from Uncle Will and buy *The Advocate* back."

We all looked at Sweyn because he was the oldest. He shook his head. "But Mamma," he said slowly, "the sale of *The Advocate* won't bring enough money for J. D. to go to school and for you to live on until we all are through college and are able to support you."

Mamma nodded. "I have thought of that. I have this big house with all its empty rooms. I am a very good cook. I shall take in boarders. With Bertha to help, we shall manage very nicely."

Katie cried out, "Mamma, how could you?"

Tom held up his hands. "But why take in boarders, Mamma? Uncle Will is a rich man. He could lend us the money needed until we are all earning enough for all our needs."

"You are your father's children," Mamma said with a note of finality in her voice. "You will stand on your own two feet. Sweyn D., when you graduate and have a practice, you will pay Grandpa Neilsen back every cent. Earnest D., when you become a successful artist, you will pay back Uncle Will every cent. Papa was a poor businessman, if not putting wealth above charity, kindness and love of his fellow-men, makes a man a poor businessman. He died rich in the love and respect of his fellow-men. And if each of you can leave the same legacy to your own children, Papa and I shall be very proud of you. As for the boarding house, I do not want to hear another word about it. My mind is made up."

Now I see Mamma with her head cocked to one side, her eyes sparkling and a gentle smile caressing her lips.

Now I hear myself asking her what she is thinking about.

Now I hear her answer, "Just borrowing Papa back for a moment."

Now I cock my head to one side and smile as I borrow both Papa and Mamma back.